Body and Soul

SARA MARTIN is a journalist who has specialized in health, fitness and alternative medicine for over ten years. During that time she has experienced most of the therapies in this book, for both research and personal interest.

Former staff writer for *Here's Health* magazine, she has also written a book on yoga (as Cheryl Isaacson).

SARA MARTIN

BODY AND SOUL

PHYSICAL THERAPIES
FOR EVERYONE

ARKANA

ARKANA

Published by the Penguin Group
27 Wrights Lane, London w8 5tz, England
Viking Penguin Inc., 40 West 23rd Street, New York, New York 10010, USA
Penguin Books Australia Ltd, Ringwood, Victoria, Australia
Penguin Books Canada Ltd, 2801 John Street, Markham, Ontario, Canada l3r 1b4
Penguin Books (NZ) Ltd, 182–190 Wairau Road, Auckland 10, New Zealand

Penguin Books Ltd, Registered Offices: Harmondsworth, Middlesex, England

First published 1989
10 9 8 7 6 5 4 3 2 1

Made and printed in Great Britian by
Richard Clay Ltd, Bungay, Suffolk
Filmset in Monophoto Plantin

To Simon

To understand the living body, we must discard mechanical concepts. The mechanisms of the bodily functioning are important, but they do not explain that functioning. An eye, for instance, is not just a camera; it is a sense organ for perceiving and an expressive organ for reacting. A heart is not just a pump; it is an organ for feeling, which a pump cannot do. We are sentient beings, which means we have the power to sense or perceive and to experience sensation or feeling. Perception is a function of the mind, which is an aspect of the body. The living body has a mind, possesses a spirit, and contains a soul.

Alexander Lowen

CONTENTS

Acknowledgements 9
Introduction 11

Aerobic Exercise 19
Aikido 33
Alexander Technique 43
Biodynamics 54
Bioenergetics 63
Dance Therapy 75
   Dancercise 81
   Eurhythmy 82
   Natural Dance 82
Feldenkrais Method 87
Massage 98
   Aromatherapy 106
   Intuitive Massage 106
   Neuro-Muscular Technique 107
   Reflexology 107
   Shiatsu 107
Pilates 110
Polarity Therapy 120
Relaxation 132
   Autogenic Training 138
   Biofeedback 140
   Hypnotherapy 141
   Meditation 141
   Progressive Relaxation 142
Rolfing 146
   Hellerwork 156
   Postural Integration 158
   Rebalancing 161
T'ai-chi 167

8 CONTENTS

Yoga 176
Other Therapies 186
  Aston-Patterning 186
  Eutony 187
  Rosen Method 191
  Trager 193

Further Reading 197
Index 201

ACKNOWLEDGEMENTS

Many people have given their time and imparted their knowledge to me in the interests of this book. I am grateful to: Harvey Burns, Anna Carlisle, Dr Malcolm Carruthers, Therese Melville van Cauwenberghe, Christopher Connolly, Guy Gladstone, Roger Golten, Alan Herdman, Karin Hofermann, Sumi Komo, John Andrew Miller, Beverley Milne, Mary Molloy, Neeraj O'Realdon, Gay Parker, Valerie Rettberg, Marion Rosen, Neerjo Sieker, Julia Swift, Phillip Young, Silke Ziehl, and to all those who spoke so freely about themselves in giving their personal views. Thank you.

I should also like to thank my editor at Penguin Books, Pamela Dix, for waiting patiently and encouragingly for the manuscript; my mother for her support; and my husband, Simon, for unceasing care.

INTRODUCTION

The therapies in this book use the physical body as a starting point. A starting point for what? Quite simply, integrating everything about you. That means they will not aim at straightening out a bad back or getting rid of headaches. They will not attempt to make you better at sport or free from arthritis. Many will, in fact, do all these things. But the difference between them and more conventional treatments lies in the intention. So, while these sorts of satisfying results may be obtained in passing, almost as 'side effects', the underlying philosophy is to look at the complete human being.

This book includes many forms of therapy, some familiar and some little known, at least in Britain. They come from many different breeding grounds, often from opposite ends of the Earth. Some involve hands-on work by the therapist, others rely on teaching and group interaction. Yet there is a rationale for inclusion that brings them all together: they can influence mind and emotions as potently as they can alter strength, shape and how you use your body.

Physical therapies treat the human body as their initial frame of reference. They consider how you stand and move, in particular. They ask questions about aches and pains, tension and strain. They all attempt to free restricted muscles, to reduce patterns of stress in the tissue. After any one of these forms of treatment you would expect to move with greater ease and grace, to breathe more fully, and to be free of the accumulated pains and minor ills of years (some so much a part of life, they have become accepted).

But there is more. The body affects the mind; the mind, the body. There is nothing fanciful about this concept, although the somewhat mechanistic divisions of Western medicine tend to compartmentalize our human functions. When a hungry man imagines food, he salivates. Before an actress goes on stage, her stomach churns. The very thought of something is enough to create a physical reaction, strong and immediate.

The interrelationship of body, mind and emotions is clear at this level, and communicated all the time. The body is a mass of signals and to some extent by our outward appearance we project a moving picture of how we feel. Most of us recognize some of these expressions of simple body language easily: the person bowed with depression, 'sad' eyes, a confident posture. The physical therapist however also reads the often-hidden, inner signs and thus helps restore to fitness far more than where he touches.

The body–mind link

The idea of treating the body to alter the mind or even consciousness is not new, although many of the therapies now used to do so are. The effects of basic physical exercise on the mind have been recognized since ancient times. In the Western tradition physical prowess, culminating in the Olympic Games, was considered to go hand in hand with the development of intellect and conscience. In the East the body was employed more in quietening the mind and remains an important part of yoga techniques for spiritual perfection.

Investigating the body-mind link began in earnest when Sigmund Freud first expounded his theories of the unconscious mind. Freud, however, relied on verbal therapy techniques and remained baffled as to why they were not successful in helping some of his patients. It was left to one of his pupils, Wilhelm Reich, to explain.

Reich, a psychiatrist and psychoanalyst, postulated that if a person lived in fear, for example, or a state of tension, perhaps as a result of his childhood conditioning, then that state would become so 'locked' into the musculature and other physical processes of the body that no amount of talking would free it. Without direct intervention involving the body, there would be no end to the 'talk cure'. Whatever insights into behaviour the patient achieved, the old ways would constantly reassert themselves because the physical frame had been moulded over the years by ingrained habits. The body effectively holds the thought-pattern trapped.

A typical observation of Reich's was that when a person began to talk about an unhappy event, one or more areas of the body would begin to tense. Often the jaw would almost seize up, as if the person were trying, without consciously being aware of it, to stop himself talking and so put an end to the pain. Reich later called this 'armouring', a graphic description of the body's attempts to protect itself from painful thoughts and emotions.

Reich's method of treating such patients was to put physical pressure on the tense spots – for instance holding a person's jaw – until they eventually gave up the struggle and released the tension by reliving whatever pent-up emotion was ossified there. His emphasis on this kind of intense physical therapy was completely unacceptable to the psychiatric and psychoanalytic authorities of the 1920s and 1930s, and he was regarded as a heretic.

Around the same time, but independent of Reich, others were also recognizing the integral relationship of mind and body. The importance of mental relaxation to physical health and the effects of expressive movement on mental health were being investigated. This new awareness of the interconnection between muscles and organs and thoughts and emotions, opened the floodgate of research and was the beginning of many of the therapies discussed in this book, as well as some of the humanistic forms of psychology out-side its scope.

One of the most crucial things to have been discovered is how early in life mental and emotional patterns are estab-lished in the body. In his book *Lifestreams* David Boadella, a therapist and follower of Reich's, says 'The tension pat-terns of the body can be looked on as a person's frozen history. If a child cannot release the tension of inescapable stress by crying, then it must continue to hold itself in tension as if the state of emergency still exists.' Many neur-otic people, he says, have a body that is in a permanent state of emergency.

In *The Body Reveals* psychotherapist Run Kurtz explains how the patterns become ingrained: 'In a healthy, open person, feeling flows easily into expression. A strong feeling of sadness spontaneously becomes a trembling jaw, tears and sobbing. In blocking the expression of sadness, we tense the jaw, chest, stomach and diaphragm, and some muscles of the throat and face – all the areas which move spontaneously when the feeling is allowed its natural out-lets.'

This is the first stage; the damage comes later. Kurtz goes on, 'If the sadness is deep and long-standing, and the blocking continues, the tension will become habit, aware-ness dims. The feeling itself may slip from consciousness and situations which arouse it may be avoided. It is this habit and lack of awareness that we are calling a block.'

This is just one example, probably familiar to nearly all of us. It becomes easy to see how many other, similar situa-tions have interrupted our past and still hamper our present. Kurtz's 'block', Reich's 'armour', may otherwise be experienced as tension, areas of holding, lack of energy, deadness, numbness or rock-hardness.

Emotional trauma may not be the whole story, but it goes a long way to explaining some of our rigidities. Often it is compounded by physical injury, which frequently seems to occur in areas where the emotional holding is worst. A highly 'protected' or 'armoured' area becomes ripe for damage much as a cut finger seems invariably to be the site of the next minor injury.

Another theme in the body-mind link is that of the life force. It is referred to directly in the chapters on polarity therapy, t'ai chi, aikido, and is involved in other therapies, such as massage and Trager. The concept is an ancient one: that we are part of an invisible energy system in which everything is interconnected, from the functioning of our smallest cell to the machinations of the universe. Through this system flows the one life force, and whenever it is disturbed there is a parallel disturbance of function in us or our physical world.

Although this force traditionally has universal significance, it is also relevant to the theories of Reich and other bodyworkers. Looking at the human body as full of this life force (clearly evident in a screaming baby, a top performing athlete or anyone using the body to the full), you can see that the damming-up of any one part of this stream blocks the flow and impedes function.

This is ideally demonstrated by the breath, perhaps the closest we come to sensing the life force at work. Intangible yet essential, it affects every part of the body. In so doing it reflects every thought and feeling we have. When it flows deeply and rhythmically, we are well. At any sign of upset, it becomes disrupted and this pattern of malfunction – whether it be shallow breathing, panic breathing, hyper-ventilation – profoundly influences our well-being. Many therapists focus a great deal of attention on the breath, since it forms the bridge between our psychology and our own life force.

But while events of the past form the body of the present, the message is that we can change the future. It is possible to drop the old patterns, to learn anew. Then we can face the world, as David Boadella says, 'without the crippling limitations of the past which have been literally embodied'.

Physical therapies

For the physical therapist your posture, the qualities of your skin, the feel of interconnective tissues that bind muscles to bone, the shape of your muscles, your very bone structure and even the subtle systems of the body – the fluids of blood and lymph with their restrictions and interruptions, respiration and the flow or holding of breath – are raw material, his framework for seeing you as a functioning whole.

Each therapy – indeed, each therapist – has its own physical focus. Rolfing, for example, homes in on the connective tissue; Alexander Technique, the relationship between head, neck and trunk; Pilates gives attention to the major muscle groups; t'ai chi to the rhythm of movement in space. These are all, ultimately, ways into the being of a person.

Very often a physical therapy bypasses words. 'The body never lies' is a phrase to which all physical therapists would heartily subscribe. Hardly ever is it necessary to talk about why and how the body has become moulded into its various postures. The work itself will reveal all. Many of the therapies mentioned in this book take the umbrella term 'bodywork' because they deal with what can be seen and felt. While what happens *to* the area on which a therapy works is important, it is what happens *through* the work that guarantees its real success.

Physical therapies can change the body, giving it the feeling of balanced unity. For some people this is the first time since childhood that they have felt such easy coordination, with its corresponding increase in vitality. Treat the body in this way and the mind cannot fail to be affected, for as the physical tensions and energy blocks dissolve, the mind becomes free from long-accumulated fears and pressures.

Physical therapists talk of the 'intelligence' or 'wisdom' of the body, meaning that it knows instinctively what is right. It is a plastic medium, ever ready to be coaxed back into shape, and, under the right learning conditions, has a marvellous ability to undo bad habits and re-train. Remove the restrictions of the years, show it the sensation of working well, and the body's response will be to recreate its own means of retaining good function.

None of the therapies in this book is invasive. That is, they cannot force your body into doing something unless you decide you want it to. A therapist will simply make suggestions, either verbally or by the sensitive use of hands, but no good practitioner will ever force his will on another. Even though a trained eye can spot immediately what changes need to be made, no one can make them but the individual. The therapist therefore often sees himself as a facilitator, awakening the client to his own abilities for harmony and self-healing.

How to choose

The book provides not only factual information about each therapy, but also a taste of what it's all about. Some readers may find themselves drawn to one therapy rather than another. Others, however, may find it difficult to know which one is right for them. The truth is that you won't know unless you try, that all the therapies bring about results in their own way, and that you don't have to stick fast to one or another. Many therapies interact favourably:

Feldenkrais with yoga, dance with Pilates, massage and relaxation with almost everything.

It is also important to realize that in most cases the therapist is what matters – possibly more than the therapy – and that it is essential to work with someone you like. The qualities of wisdom and understanding are not much talked about in an age of qualifications and diplomas, but these are precisely what a physical therapist needs. Empathy, sensitivity, insight, trustworthiness and, of course, a thorough knowledge of the therapy from a technical point of view are all vital. All the therapists listed in the book are of a professional standard. Personal recommendation is, of course, the best guide: seeing a friend transformed says more for the therapy and the therapist than anything else.

Don't be afraid to ask questions, and do rely on your intuition and spend time before deciding on a particular course of treatment. While some of the therapies mentioned can usually be tried first on a casual basis – such as yoga, Feldenkrais, massage – others demand a commitment, as with the ten Rolfing sessions or Hellerwork. Once you have decided on a course of action, give it a fair trial, going regularly for at least two or three months, especially in the case of therapies whose results take time to build up, such as Pilates, t'ai chi, aikido and Alexander Technique. The therapist will give recommendations.

'He' and 'she' as used in the text are interchangeable. Particular usage simply suggests that someone of that sex was interviewed for the chapter, not that they form the majority for that therapy. Male and female practitioners can be found in most fields and every therapy is open to all. Similarly, the use of therapist/practitioner/teacher and patient/client/student, while appropriate, do not imply any rigid role or structure.

AEROBIC

EXERCISE

What is it?

Aerobic simply means any activity that uses oxygen. Although some people regard the idea of 'aerobics' with suspicion, feeling that it implies something tough and strenuous, they are actually performing aerobics much of the time. Just walking to the shops or along the office corridor is an aerobic activity. It makes the muscles work harder, increasing their need for oxygen and thus demanding that the heart beats faster, pumping blood, which carries the oxygen. Of course, a gentle stroll will do little to enhance these systems. Aerobics is effective largely in the degree to which it increases oxygen uptake.

The most valuable exercises, aerobically, are those that involve a sustained effort and make you feel a certain amount of 'push'. They include steady running, jogging, fast and uphill walking, swimming, cycling, skipping and the all-purpose exercise class. These differ from anaerobic exercises, in which increased oxygen uptake is not a major factor – activities like squash, tennis, gymnastics and even sprinting, where the effort is in explosive bursts and may be over so quickly that athletes even hold their breath.

Most forms of exercise are a mixture of aerobic and anaerobic. For example, marathon running is almost 100 per cent aerobic, but the first mile and the finishing burst may be anaerobic. One of the main aims of a graduated exercise programme is to enable heart, lungs and muscles to handle ever-increasing amounts of work without dipping into 'oxygen debt', which prevents the waste products of muscular effort, such as lactic acid, being washed away by the bloodstream.

Aerobic exercise as therapy

Why include sports-type activity in a book about therapy? Because regular aerobic exercise has very real therapeutic value. Obviously, an unfit person exercising for the first time, or doing it sporadically while allowing the body to 'run down' in between times, will feel it as a punishment rather than a benefit. But aerobic exercise works its wonders surprisingly fast. Over time, the regular aerobic exerciser generally boasts lower blood pressure, reduced fat levels in the blood and less body fat than his less active friend. Some researchers, such as Dr Kenneth Cooper, the American who popularized the term 'aerobics', say it helps slow down the ageing process by charging cells with regular supplies of life-giving oxygen.

Although aerobic exercise is primarily associated with strengthening the heart and lungs, your whole body benefits. As aerobic exercise improves the circulation of blood, more parts of the body receive nourishment and are cleansed of toxic waste. The liver and other major organs work better, as do the nervous and hormonal systems, as your body becomes more efficient. In short, everything becomes balanced and toned. When the body machine is in good working order, you will also find it easier to shape up and stay slim, with naturally trim muscles rather than the tired, flaccid look that comes from too rigid attempts to lose weight. More than all this, you will exude a certain sort of energy, a real vitality.

Exercise also encourages the brain to release endorphins, the body's natural pain-killers, which act similarly to the drug morphine. Other hormone effects are thought to be

Aerobic exercise can bring vitality and exhilaration.

responsible for the 'runner's high' experienced by people addicted to regular exercise. This addiction is a healthy one and can in time replace less beneficial ones such as smoking and overeating.

Regular exercisers are less susceptible not only to the so-called normal physical ills such as colds, flu and degenerative disease, but also to depression, irritability and other common stress-related psychological ills. Indeed, there are many stories of people giving up tranquillizers and antidepressants in favour of regular bouts of exercise.

Herein lies the truth of exercise as therapy. It's fine to have your body in good shape and working order, but that can never be an end in itself. It's what it brings to you as a person that is all-important. Here we are beyond the realms of the scientific, for though studies prove the kind of physical effects mentioned earlier, they cannot measure the effects of feeling better, coping more easily, releasing tension or increasing confidence.

No amount of reading about all the benefits of exercise will give them to you. The only way to get them is by actually exercising.

The problems of exercise

The most prevalent problem is getting started. Of course you will probably feel worse before you feel better. The body used to getting only from chair to car, with its flabby muscles and sluggish heart and lungs, will protest strongly at any exertion. Do not be deterred. Once through the initial agony, the miracle will happen. Suddenly your body will be crying out for exercise and you will feel worse if you don't do it. Miss out on your regular routine, whatever it may be, and the rot will begin to set in. This time, though, you will feel it instantly and, instead of letting it progress insidiously, you will take action again.

There are a couple other problems that may discourage people from starting to exercise. The chief anxiety is that exercise is dangerous: you can die from jogging or suffer permanent muscle injury through 'going for the burn'. Yes, there are dangers – predominantly from exercise unsuitable for your age and fitness level. Bear in mind that while largely beneficial, exercise is also a stress. It must be used carefully and with common sense. Leave the real hard stuff to the professionals – they thrive on it. For most of us, the price of a short struggle with lethargy is cheap for the sheer enjoyment of well-being.

Taking care

First, then, when should you exercise and when not? It is generally recommended that anyone who is not used to regular exercise should have a medical check-up before starting to exercise again (see Table 1, below). This is also important if you answer yes to any of the following questions.

- Are you overweight?
- Do you smoke or drink?
- Do you have a high-sugar diet?
- Do you eat a lot of meat and/or other saturated fats?
- Is there a history of heart disease or congenital heart problems in your family?
- Do you have any circulatory problems, such as angina or varicose veins?
- Do you have any respiratory problems, such as hay fever, asthma or bronchitis?
- Are you generally subject to a high level of mental, physical or emotional stress?

Table 1 Pre-exercise precautions for the unfit

Age	Medical recommendations
under 30	general check-up within preceding year
30–39	general check-up and resting ECG within preceding three months
40–59	general check-up, resting ECG and exercise stress test within preceding three months
over 59	thorough medical examination, resting ECG and exercise stress test immediately before starting exercise programme

Your GP can give you a standard check-up and arrange for you to have a resting electrocardiogram (ECG), which measures the electrical activity of your heart, and exercise stress test, which measures the activity of your heart while you are exercising. Do be completely honest with the doctor about the reasons for the check-up and the kind of exercise programme you are contemplating. What should you do if you have any history of illness? 'You can still exercise', believes expert Julia Swift. 'Back pain, joint pain, can be eradicated with regular sessions of exercise. In fact, you can even exercise after a heart attack.' But she adds words of warning to these optimistic statements. 'Check out the exercise with your medical practitioner, always exercise under supervision – for instance, in a class with a properly qualified teacher – and let the instructor know of any past illness.'

If necessary, too, the exercise should be customized to your condition. You and your exercise advisor should discuss the length of time since your illness, whether you are still recuperating and using the exercise as part of that process, or whether you and your doctor consider you have regained full activity. In fact, when considering what exercise is best, you should never overlook any major illness, accidents or injuries even if they occurred way in the past. They may have taken their toll, and physical injury can leave an area vulnerable even though trouble-free in everyday life.

The best way to gauge whether your exercise routine is working for you is the standard pulse test. First check your resting pulse. This is the pulse first thing in the morning, before you have had any kind of exertion – before getting out of bed, and definitely before eating or drinking tea or coffee, is ideal. The easiest way to take your pulse is to grasp your left wrist with your right hand so that the middle finger and thumb meet on the inside of the wrist. Use the first two fingers of the right hand to find the pulse – it will be just below the base of the thumb. Looking at a clock or a watch with a second hand, count the number of beats for ten seconds and multiply by six.

Table 2 is a general guide to your fitness.

Table 2 Resting pulse rate

Age		20–29	30–39	40–49	50 +
Good:	men	59–69	63–71	65–73	67–75
	women	71–77	73–79	75–79	77–83
Fair:	men	70–85	72–85	74–89	76–89
	women	78–95	80–97	80–98	84–99
Poor:	men	86 +	86 +	90 +	90 +
	women	96 +	98 +	99 +	100 +

If your resting pulse rate is over 100 beats a minute, you should consult your doctor.

Next, take your pulse during exercise. Be sure to do it without stopping – you must keep moving so the pulse doesn't take a sudden dive. The maximum safe heart rate decreases with age: at 20 a fit heart should be capable of about 180 beats a minute without damage, declining by about 10 beats a minute with every additional 10 years of age. During a work-out a fit person's heart should reach a steady three-quarters of the maximum for his or her age for at least fifteen minutes. If you are not fit, your pulse rate won't reach this level. If at any time you feel dizziness, pain or nausea, stop exercising immediately.

Your exercise pulse rate is not only a gauge of your fitness, but can also indicate what kind of exercise programme you should follow. For example, if just going up a couple of flights of stairs sends your pulse racing to its maximum, it would not be sensible for you to start jogging or any other strenuous activity. In fact, you should be careful not to over-exercise and to take adequate rests during exercise to bring your pulse down. Use your common sense about

Warm-ups are very important.

your body. That doesn't mean sitting back and letting the rot set in, just increasing the challenge gradually and at a non-damaging rate.

The third step in assessing whether your exercise programme is working is to find your recovery rate. This is the speed at which your pulse returns to normal (about fifteen beats a minute higher than the resting pulse) after exercising. Exercise for three minutes. Take your pulse as soon as you stop. Rest and take your pulse at thirty second intervals until it is normal. Make a note of how long this takes.

Test all your pulse rates again after a few weeks of your exercise programme: as you get fitter your resting pulse rate should decrease, your exercise pulse rate gradually increase and become steadier, and your recovery rate increase.

Exercise is best done on an empty stomach. The process of digestion concentrates blood flow to the stomach and intestines, and exercise, which diverts circulation, can bring on headaches and nausea. Allow at least one hour between eating or drinking and exercising, more if the meal has been heavy and the intended exercise strenuous.

The warm-up and cool-down are absolutely essential. A warm-up ensures that the blood pumping increases gradually, avoiding sudden strain and shock to the heart. It also raises overall body temperature, helping muscles to relax and lengthen, thus preventing injuries such as sprains and torn ligaments. Good warm-ups are stretching and flopping, touching your toes or as close as you can reach (bend your knees if you feel any strain in your back); bringing the knees up to the chest; swinging round from the waist with arms outstretched – all the old PT favourites done slowly and without strain.

Start your actual aerobic session slowly and carefully, and wait until your breathing is easy and rhythmical before pushing yourself.

At the end of your session slow down gradually. If you come to an abrupt stop, blood that has been pushed to the extremities of the body will be unable to return to the heart and recirculate normally. This may cause a lack of blood in the brain and the possibility of dizziness or fainting. The cool-down also reduces any tendency towards stiffness, as it helps the body pump away lactic acid (a waste product resulting from the chemical reaction involved in muscle exertion) – a primary cause of post-exercise ache.

A matter of choice

What's your exercise? It's important to find something that fits your personality, physical type and life-style, or you will quickly tire of what becomes an imposition. Slim, slight people may take to running. The seriously overweight may prefer informal exercise sessions at home, with the help of an exercise video. They may also feel more comfortable with activities in which weight is supported, such as swimming or cycling.

If you like routine and discipline, set aside regular sessions at an aerobics class or a gym that offers specific aerobic circuit training.* Make sure that there are qualified professionals in charge and talk to them before committing

* The weight training usually offered in a gym is not aerobic.

yourself, asking questions about their training background. If you have any reservations, look for a more satisfactory venue.

Exercise can be a solitary business or it can be a means to a good social life. Joining a class often forges supportive friendships as barriers break down in the communal effort.

What to expect

Although, as we've said, many kinds of exercise are truly aerobic, to many people 'exercise' means 'aerobics'. Since the introduction of the original 'keep fit' class (which is still going strong) there has been a major explosion of exercise classes. The redoubtable Eileen Fowler brought the concept of movement into everyone's living rooms through her TV programme. The idea of a more aggressive exercise programme came to the fore with the popularization of the Canadian Air Force system, followed by the mother of aerobics as we know it, Jane Fonda. Because of the vast publicity machine surrounding stars such as she, aerobics quickly acquired a glamour image, and masses of unfit people strained themselves in unsuitable aerobics classes burning to attain instant fitness and a beautiful body.

The good news is that exercise is now orientated less towards an instant, glamorous body transformation and more towards whole body fitness at a gradual pace. Straining to keep up is no longer acceptable, learning how your individual body should feel and behave in each exercise is. Music and choreography are better organized and many teachers are better trained to understand both the physical and psychological needs of exercisers. Ideally, classes include dietary and nutritional advice, particularly for people who want to lose weight, and cater for special needs, such as those of pregnant students, who need to follow a modified exercise routine.

While there is still room for the Fonda-type 'high-impact' aerobics, it is not recommended for beginners. Only if you are used to exercise, are fit and know your body well should you attempt this type of energetic routine. It is better to start with a general body conditioning class, based around the fluid movements of dance and designed to stretch and strengthen muscle groups while giving gentle stimulus to heart and lungs.

In the middle come low-impact aerobics. As the name suggests, these exercises are more energetic than basic conditioning, but while working heart and lungs faster and pushing circulation more strongly, they lack the tempo of high-impact aerobics. Whatever the type of aerobics, the class must start and end with warm-up and cool-down routines.

Taking three classes (about one and a quarter hours each) a week is recommended for best results. Julia Swift says the minimum requirement to see changes, physical and psychological, is two classes a week for twelve weeks, continuing regularly for as long as you want to stay healthy and vital.

If you decide to go in for the new aerobics, remember to wear comfortable (preferably worn-in) training shoes that will cushion your weight. Designer leotards are not required, but clothing that does not impede movement and can absorb the sweat is essential.

Do we need aerobics?

Yes, more than ever before. Life is becoming increasingly sedentary and, while no one would wish to do away with labour-saving devices like the washing machine or car, there is no doubt that most of us simply do not have enough physical activity in our everyday lives. The fact is, our bodies are made for activity, and when we don't get it, we are abusing ourselves. Therefore we have to create special 'work-out' times set aside from the daily routine. Even a half-hour every other day makes a difference to the efficiency and alertness with which we perform our other tasks.

Personal views

● *Maureen, 42, antiques dealer*. I've been going to an aerobics class for about nine years. I get withdrawal symptoms if I don't go now. I had been doing yoga and then 'keep fit', and wanted something more vigorous. I've definitely made a great breakthrough in fitness since I've been doing this. I find all parts of my body get exercised in this class.

I wanted to lose weight, too. You won't lose weight just doing exercise, but you'll definitely do so if you go on a diet at the same time. I lost a stone and went down from size 14 to size 10. I also firmed and toned up all over. Mind you, if you don't keep it up, it's murder, you get stiff again. I often think I daren't miss a class because it would make my muscles stiffen up. I go twice a week or three times if possible.

Though the class is purely physical, it gives you more. I think it gives you confidence in yourself, as you're doing your body so much good. I feel on top of the world after a class, never tired, but exhilarated. It stimulates my whole body and mind.

● *Jackie, 46, market stall-holder*. I've had seven years going to an aerobics class. I did squash and tennis before that. This is totally different to sport, it's non-competitive – that's what I like about it. It's made me much more aware of my body and I feel alive and confident in a way that I never did before. The confidence was unexpected. I thought the class would help my body, but I didn't expect it to do so much psychologically.

Even if I feel awful, I drag myself along. If you're tired before, you still feel better after a session. It's actually very relaxing. Whatever problems you come in with seem to be forgotten or in perspective after a class. You can't think about two things at once – while you're in there, it's solid concentration on the exercises and everything else goes. It's been a fifty-fifty effect for me, mentally and physically.

It's also imposed a discipline on my life. I do it religiously. I don't understand why, even when I feel lazy I still go. It goes back to that feeling of being mentally uplifting; you can start off feeling really down, but it always lifts you up.

● *Sharon, 24, systems analyst*. Why do I groan my way out of bed at 7 a.m. three times a week to get down to the pool before I go to work? It's always a hard question to answer at the time, but I know why later in the day. I just feel alive. Swimming has a way of getting you thoroughly exercised. I feel as if no part has been left out, everything has energy flowing through it, yet at the same time, it's very relaxed. With swimming, you can take it as lazily as you like, or when you're feeling more like pushing yourself, you can do that too. But it never seems as if you are using any force or strain; it's more like a good long relaxing stretch in every fibre of your being.

It's wonderful for your circulation. I can go along on the coldest of winter days and glow for hours when everyone else is turning the heating up. I have my own central heating system. I also think it keeps me toned up, at least, I don't seem to have any flab or bulges, though I eat as much as I want.

The worst thing is when for some reason I leave out a session. I actually start aching when I don't exercise. I feel uncomfortable, don't know what to do with myself. When I'm tired or tense, it's excellent to go for a swim, it takes away those feelings straight away. Even if you're still tired afterwards, it's a different sort of tiredness, you can relax naturally instead of having that horrible sort of over-active mind that often goes with mental exhaustion. For me it's the only way of keeping fit.

Where to go

Your local library will have information about gyms and health clubs. Also check the Yellow Pages, and ask at the local sports centre (find its number in the telephone book).

Asset
202 The Avenue
Kennington, Oxford OX1 5RN
Tel: 0865-736066
Information about qualified
health and exercise teachers

Keep Fit Association
16 Upper Woburn Place
London WC1H 0QC
Tel: 01-387-4349

Medau Society of Great
Britain and Northern Ireland
8b Robson House
East Street
Epsom, Surrey KT17 1HH
Tel: 03727-29056

Margaret Morris Movement
Suite 3/4
39 Hope Street
Glasgow G2 6AG

What is it?

Aikido is a martial art, but its application lies far beyond the ability to defend oneself and confound one's opponent. The name means 'way of divine harmony' and this method of subduing attack is, at heart, a system for mental and spiritual growth based on an understanding of the flow of '*ki*', as the Japanese call the life force. According to Morihei Ueshiba, the founder of aikido, 'The secret of aikido is to harmonize ourselves with the movement of the universe and to bring ourselves into accord with the universe itself.'

Aikido does not require aggression or even physical strength – its chief quality is the use of the minimum possible force. Even when defending himself, the exponent is responsible for the safety of the attacker and must ensure he is not injured. Therefore, the aikidoist does not confront an attack, but blends with it, an approach that affects the whole of life. The practitioner thus learns how to live in a way that harmonizes with events and circumstances, alert yet relaxed. Because its aim is harmonious blending, not the use of force, aikido is considered a 'soft' martial art.

The origins of aikido

Legend has it that the martial arts were developed 5,000 years ago by Tibetan monks. Although forbidden to cause harm or to carry weapons, these travelling holy men needed some way of defending themselves against attack by robbers and soldiers as they went from village to village. They

Blending with and disarming an attacker.

studied the human body as a natural defence system. They hardened their hands by plunging them into buckets of sand, rice and pebbles; they toughened their feet and legs by kicking at wooden posts. They identified key points of the body where attack would be most effective and originated a repertoire of defensive punches, kicks, locks and throws, the basis of what became the 'hard' martial arts, or combat sports: karate, kung fu, taekwando and judo.

The cream of the martial artists in Japan were the samurai warriors, professional killers trained in the complete range of the fighting arts. Morihei Ueshiba was the great-grandson of one of Japan's most famous samurai warriors and so it was natural that having been ill as a child, he started studying the martial arts in order to rebuild his health. He worked with many of the greatest teachers of the time, mastering one system of fighting after another. But he felt strongly that everything he learned seemed to encourage a 'might is right' mentality.

Increasingly he spent long periods in isolated meditation and prayer, trying to become 'one with the universe'. Aikido has its beginings in what Ueshiba described as a moment of divine revelation, when he suddenly 'knew' that a true martial art was based on love, reverence and protection of all things, not on the ability to hit others harder and faster than they could hit you. His semi-mystical views were scorned by the established teachers of the day, but his outstanding demonstrations won them over. He founded aikido in the 1920s, when he was in his forties, and continued to teach well into his eighties.

What to expect

Aikido practice takes place in a *dojo*, or training hall, where the floor is covered with soft mats. The aikido *dojo* is not as formal and regimented as a karate training hall, but has a friendly air of discipline and concentration, which is important for safety.

Students wear loose, comfortable clothing, traditionally baggy pyjama-type suits of heavy white cotton, tied with a belt round the middle. Belt colours signify the student's grade, from the white or red of the beginner to the coveted black of the master. No shoes or socks are worn. Feet and hands are expected to be clean, with short nails. All jewellery is removed, as even a glancing blow with a small ring can tear someone's skin.

The essence of all martial arts is that everyone, no matter what their grade, is treated with respect. The black belt can learn as much from dealing with an awkward white belt as from smooth practice with someone of his own standard.

When the teacher explains a movement to the class, it is traditional and respectful for everyone to stop and give their undivided attention. This means a portion of every class is spent 'sitting'; really, kneeling with the legs tucked underneath the body. Often this is one of the most uncomfortable aspects of aikido for new students. However it is never rigidly enforced, and gradually becomes easier as muscles and tendons stretch. Most classes also include a period of seated meditation and breathing to calm the mind and body.

One of the first exercises shown to beginners proves dramatically how the mind can affect the body. This exercise is known as the 'unbendable arm', and is done in pairs. While standing, one person holds out his strongest arm in front of him, palm up and slightly bent at the elbow. The other person places one hand in the crook of the first person's elbow and, using as much strength as possible, with the other hand tries to force the arm to bend in the middle.

Naturally, this becomes a straightforward contest of strength, with much grimacing and clenching, and is often quite painful. After both have recovered their breath, the two repeat the exercise. This time, the person having his arm bent makes no attempt to resist. Instead, he relaxes and imagines the arm is empty like a hosepipe, until the *ki* starts flowing and changes the pipe into something of enormous direction and strength. The difference is always astonishing. Without any effort, and certainly without expending physical energy or brute force, the weakest person will be able to resist all attempts to bend his arm. Strangely, once you start to think about what is happening, the arm will collapse; another example of the mind affecting the body.

This same principle is then applied in many different sorts of situation. Once the unbendable arm is mastered, students move on to exercises in various positions, testing maintenance of mind-body coordination after falling or rolling on the floor. They quickly find relaxing while sitting or lying down is one thing, but staying relaxed when taken by surprise or in unbalanced postures is not so easy.

One thing every new aikidoist has to learn and practise diligently is how to fall. The most daunting obstacle to overcome is simply the fear of falling. Many people associate falling with inevitable injury and since childhood have avoided it. Even on a padded mat, falling in the wrong way can cause injury, so part of every class is devoted to the practice of rolling breakfalls, a dynamic version of forward rolls. Here the energy of the fall, or the contact between body and mat, is dissipated safely by the circular movement of the roll. In an aikido setting rolling falls and hitting the soft mat can be quite enjoyable and add to the sense of freedom and self-confidence the art gives. Aikido is noted for its circular throws and elegant movement, which can look rhythmic and almost as if in slow motion when done by experts.

Once you have learnt that falling can be painless and you can relax and cooperate with your partner, aikido becomes

***Randori*: an aikidoist repulses four attackers.**

a gentle dance. 'Attacking' someone, only to be led in a series of graceful circular movements before finding yourself gently collapsing on the ground, is a confusing and surrendering experience at the same time, and often very humorous.

The most dramatic test of composure is demonstrated when advanced aikidoists practice the free-style *randori*, with one person facing random attacks from three or four people at once. The result is a spectacular, whirling ballet, with people flying through the air and landing gracefully to attack again and again. At the centre of the storm, unhurried and unruffled, spins the person supposedly being attacked. At its best it can be a magical sight.

The level of skill required to stay calm and deal effortlessly with multiple 'attackers' like this comes only after years of practice. It can take ten years or more to work through all the grades and many people claim learning starts in earnest only at black belt level, which has its own grading system.

Ki aikido

This version of aikido was formulated by one of Ueshiba's pupils, Koichi Tohei, who formed the Ki Society International in 1971. Tohei put more emphasis on *ki* than conventional classes, and developed separate exercises to train students in its use. He formulated four basic rules: keep the mind calm and concentrated at one point in the abdomen, relax completely, keep weight underside and extend *ki*.

To help 'extend *ki*', Tohei explained, students can think of it as a beam of light or a stream of water. Thus, instead of being an abstract concept, it becomes more of a reality, which can be moved around the body at will. Ki clubs affiliated to the Ki Society stress the relaxation and energy work from the very beginning, whereas conventional aikido classes take a more overtly physical line at first, and teach breathing, relaxation and the use of *ki* as the student makes progress.

Who benefits?

Since age, size and strength count for little in aikido, it is suitable for everyone. Women train alongside men, older people with children. Physical condition is no barrier – you do not have to be particularly fit or dexterous when you start, as the practice itself imparts everything you need. The *ki* exercises promote glowing health and fitness.

American author George Leonard, who achieved his black belt at the age of 52 after six years' training, describes how he felt on the way:

The results shatter some cultural stereotypes. Older people are supposed to be stiffer, less resilient than younger people, but as my years of aikido have passed,

I've become steadily more supple and flexible. Older people are supposed to heal less readily, but my injuries have healed just as fast as, and sometimes faster than, anyone else's. Older people are supposed to be resistant to learning, set in their ways, but I feel I'm a much faster learner now than in my youth. The fact of the matter is I can do everything now that I could do in my twenties and a lot that I wouldn't have dreamed of doing.

Personal view

● *Simon, 35, journalist.* Firstly I was looking for a way of defending myself, as I was bullied as a small kid. I'd also done a lot of sports such as cycling and running and though I got a lot out of them, I was becoming stiffer and less flexible. So I pursued martial arts, as I wanted to do something that seemed to teach people to use their body in the most efficient way.

Originally I tried judo, karate and kung-fu, but I soon found that a good big person always beats a good small person. Then I found out about a martial art that seemed to embody the spirit I was looking for, that is, simply that the person most in tune with himself would have a non-violent way of protecting himself.

The thing that really impressed me about aikido was seeing the old films of Ueshiba in action in his seventies and eighties. No one could lay a finger on him and he was still obviously agile and quick-thinking even though he was an old man. I thought if you can have that mobility and power at that age, obviously this is a martial art you don't have to be 6'3" and 300 pounds to do.

The first thing I remember being struck with when

I went to an aikido class was the complete difference to any other martial arts class I'd been to before. No one was hitting anybody or throwing each other about or pinning people to the ground. Instead, we learned how unstable we were doing ordinary things like standing up and sitting down. I remember being very surprised at how easy it was to become off balance just by moving your attention into your head.

I also found that you learn by doing it – the more you do, the quicker you learn. I started by going once a week, but in between I'd forgot what I'd picked up. You can make progress but you really need two lessons a week. It's quite easy to learn – it's based on rhythm and repetition. You can spend an hour or two practising the same movement, slightly differently each time, continually trying to sense what you're doing with your body, where the energy is flowing. At the same time you are dealing with another person as well, so you have to work out how you are interrelating with this other energy field.

It quickly affected the rest of my life. One of the main points is that it just doesn't work if you're tense, so you have to learn to be perfectly relaxed while sitting, standing and then when someone is 'attacking' – which can mean approaching or confronting you in daily life. It's a great thing once you can stay relaxed on the move, as you can use it walking down the road, driving the car or in any situation. It translates very easily into anything you want to do and you find yourself doing things with the minimum of effort.

The spirit of aikido also teaches that in order to deal with someone coming at you, you don't get in their way. Whereas, for instance, in karate if someone was walking towards your space, you would defend it with a punch or a kick, the first thing you do in aikido is give that space away. So in most aikido movements you try to put yourself in the other person's position, you actually turn alongside them to do a throw. You can translate that into the rest of life and see the other person's point of view and go the same way together.

Another thing I like is that you don't have to be fit to do it, but it does get you fit. You spend a lot of time falling on the floor and getting up again, that's good exercise in itself. You develop a relaxed and flexible body and mind.

Where to go

Ki Federation of Great
Britain
Room 4
NatWest Bank Chambers
Victoria Street
Burnham-on-Sea
Somerset TA8 1AN
Tel: 0278-781166

For clubs in the United
Kingdom Aikido
Federation,
contact:
Martial Arts Commission
15 Deptford Broadway
London SE8 4PE
Tel: 01-691-3433

ALEXANDER

TECHNIQUE

What is it?

The Alexander Technique is a form of deep physical release. It is difficult to describe because it is essentially an
experience, and different for everyone according to their
own personal strains and stresses. The aim is to develop a
'felt' consciousness, a new awareness of body use.

A basic principle of the technique is that our sensory
perception is usually dulled and therefore inaccurate. When
an Alexander teacher gives an instruction to hold the head
up, for example, the usual response is to throw it back. Our
own feelings about our bodies are so suspect, argued F.
Matthias Alexander, the originator of the technique, that
we need re-educating before we can begin to recognize
posture that is completely free from self-imposed restrictions.

Any experience of the technique is deeply relaxing, although that sense may turn into frustration when you seem
to have either no physical awareness of various parts of the
body or refuse steadfastly to 'let go' of them when you do!
A common response to initial lessons is to fall asleep: we
put a great deal of strain into most activities, and when this
overlying stress layer is dissolved, our exhaustion is revealed.

Another early difficulty in learning the technique is finding the balance between unconsciousness and tension. The
first step is developing attention and sensitivity to what's
going on in the body. While it is easy to recognize gross

misuse – slouching, twisting legs, hunched shoulders – the technique concentrates on the tiny, subtle movements of daily life, such as those involved in picking up a book or sitting on a chair. These are the movements that are most likely to deceive. 'He gets what he feels is the right position,' said Alexander of one pupil, 'but that only means he's getting the position which fits in with his defective co-ordination.'

Once we recognize this faulty awareness that gives such false messages, we are clear to let go of the old habit patterns, or mechanical use of self, as Alexander called it. Herein lies the brain-knotting elusiveness of the technique. It takes guidance, practice and, above all, constant awareness – or attention, in Alexander parlance – to realize what's really right instead of what we just thought was right.

The next step is learning to stop the misuse. It's all too easy at this stage to relax too deeply and give up the new-found attentiveness in sleep. An alternative reaction, also wrong, is to re-tense the muscles in an attempt to change. This is why the directions instruct you to 'think' your way to reorganizing the pattern of use. In that instant when the brain takes over from automatic physical response comes the moment of choice. Here you can experience the connection between thinking and activity, and give yourself the freedom to undo an old, unconstructive habit.

Inhibition – a positive concept

Alexander teachers speak of 'inhibiting' an action and of 'conscious control'. Both of these seem outmoded concepts in a post-Freudian world, but Alexander defended their use. He was talking about transformation, from a state of unawareness and self-hindrance to one in which a person could fulfil his highest potential. This could be achieved, he said, only by developing the brain and especially the

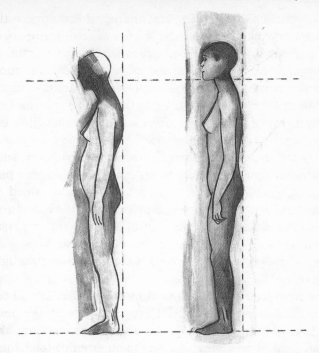

Alexander work emphasizes directing the body 'up' and 'back'.

reasoning powers. Greater consciousness would lead to less unconscious, busy 'doing'.

One pitfall while learning the technique is that of 'end-gaining'. Once you grasp the basic idea, the normal reaction is to concentrate on the end result. This in itself distracts attention. The Alexander Technique is a complete re-education, a continuous process during which you watch all the time. A few lessons can teach you how to release, for example, a pattern of misuse that may be causing painful muscle tension. But unless you understand the means whereby the pattern was created, the old use will recur.

Alexander's advice was to learn to think in terms of

continuing activity – of what you are doing now rather than what you have done or plan to do. In many ways Alexander was ahead of his time. He pre-dated the 'human potential' movement with its emphasis on self-knowledge and concentrating on the here-and-now, much of which is borrowed from Eastern traditions and especially Zen enlightenment. The sense of quietness and tranquillity that can come through the Alexander Technique is very similar, and the non-reaction to stimulus is comparable, to an observing, watchful, meditative state.

F. Matthias Alexander

F. Matthias Alexander was a strict rationalist and developed the work with no reference to any of these spiritual ideas, although he was something of a philosopher, as his four books show. He was born in Tasmania, Australia, in 1869. By the time he was 19 he had become known in Melbourne for his Shakespearian recitals. At this point he was plagued with a voice problem: his sound would weaken and sometimes disappear during a performance. Doctors were no help. Then Alexander took matters into his own hands. He observed, with the aid of mirrors, a habit of pulling his head back and down. Although the movement was comparatively small, it effectively interfered with his voice production. He devoted the next five years to realigning the relationship between his head, neck and trunk, and formulating the method – or 'work', as he called it – familiar to every Alexander student today.

After the age of 25, Alexander devoted his life to teaching. At first he concentrated mainly on others whose voices were their careers: actors and singers. In 1904 he went to London on the recommendation of a well-known surgeon (the medical profession was by then showing interest in his findings). He continued to teach his methods, established a children's school and, following a stroke in 1947, successfully recovered the use of his left arm and leg through diligent application of his technique. He died in 1955, aged 86.

What to expect

Sessions take about an hour and are largely passive – that is, you don't have to do anything except follow instructions. What is necessary, though, is the sincere attempt to focus the mind on what you are doing as far as is humanly possible.

Your teacher will talk much of the time, reminding you to 'let the head come forwards and upwards', to 'let the back lengthen and widen' or 'see that you're not pulling the head backwards'. You are required to move only the merest amount – a favourite exercise to give beginners is getting up from a chair. You may also be asked to lie down on a flat couch and to become aware of how you have positioned your body, or to stand with feet a little apart and simply bend slightly at the knees.

None of these is an unthinking action. All require full concentration and an intense lead-up period to ensure that the body is in a state of ease and the mind watchful and observant before any degree of movement is undertaken. Even when little seems to be accomplished, much will have gone on. You may have periods of boredom, of discomfort, of suddenly recognizing an area of long-held tension. Afterwards you may feel sleepy, light-headed or wide awake. As the sessions continue and inner tensions are dropped, you would expect to feel better after each one and to be able to retain its positive effects for longer periods on your own.

People usually want to know how many sessions they

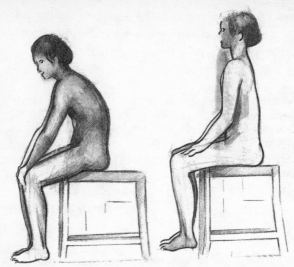

A slumped sitting position contrasts strongly with a balanced one.

will need. Since individual responses to the technique vary, it is hard for a teacher to tell until she sees you in action, as it were, for a few weeks. The usual number of sessions is 20 to 30, after which the student should have absorbed enough of the technique to be able to apply it all the time.

Why we need the Alexander Technique

Although Alexander did so much to create awareness of how people deviate from graceful, unrestricted movement, he was unable to answer categorically the ever-present question: why do we so painfully misuse the human form? Speculation continues to this day. Studies show that deterioration begins around the age of 4. Alexander thought it to be an integral part of the evolutionary process. Growth towards 'civilization', he conjectured, has made us uneven and unbalanced. Mental activity has continued at the cost of physical deterioration. This has created a split whereby we interfere with the co-ordinated use of the mechanism as a whole, in particular the muscular system. The only hope for the future, he thought, is to 'come into that supreme inheritance which is the complete control of our own potentialities'.

Any physical tension takes its toll on the body and the technique can be learned by anyone interested in improving his body use and being relieved of the aches and pains that come with chronic misuse. It is open to all and with its help anyone who sits, stands or moves can do so with a new grace and poise. It still echoes its beginnings in its particular relevance to performing artists. Singers and musicians find it especially helpful because their professions impose unnatural restrictions on the body. The very effort of holding a violin, for example, can cause chronic physical stress unless the performer learns to manage his instrument with the minimum imposition on his natural freedom of movement. Many performers have discovered an extra dimension to their self-expression by gaining awareness, and the ability to let go, of the restrictions previously implicit in their art.

Personal views

- *David, 42, dentist*. I first became involved in the Alexander Technique three years ago. The reason was my back problem. I'm a dentist and the chairside work had led to a prolapsed disc. I had my first operation in 1982, when they scraped out the discs that had broken down. Then they had to link my pelvis up to my lumbar spine and keep the area stable.

  After that I went back to work but was still in pain,

and they told me the fusion hadn't solidified. They tried to tidy things up with another operation, but after that I was totally immobilized for about a year – I could get up for only about an hour a day.

Then I went to see a surgeon who dealt with failed operations like mine, and he decided it was best to do another operation involving combined anterior and posterior fusion of the pelvis onto the spinal column. That meant two major operations in one, then putting metal rods in. After that I was in bed for six months, and by then I'd had enough of operations. The fusion had worked this time, but the pain was still intense. They didn't really know why, except that it was muscle spasm.

Well, then one of my colleagues who knew about the Alexander Technique organized a lecture and I went to take lessons. The Alexander teacher put me on the table and did the normal things and I was completely pain-free, something that had been impossible before. I continued going and it was great while I was being worked on, but I was in horrendous agony on the train going there and then it would start hurting on the way back again. I thought, well this is crazy, taking the pain out and then making it worse.

So then I found another teacher who lived near me, and this time things improved a lot. Partly it was because I didn't have the long train journey and also she had a different approach; she was gentle and undemanding and didn't try to achieve too much too soon.

My progress continued all the time. I still have problems, but nothing like I did when I started. The metal rods have been taken out and I am able to get around. I'm taking fewer pain-killers and I can sustain activities longer. I can't treat patients any more; there would be no way of avoiding the awkward position that had started the trouble in the first place. Sitting for any period of time pulls me down, too. Even when I go fishing it takes me two days to recover.

When I have an Alexander lesson, I can feel the muscles being released and re-educated to the right length, but it all has to be done in tiny steps or there's a terrific reaction and spasm afterwards. Often different areas become uncomfortable, then feel great again.

None of the medical profession has shown any real understanding of the problems or tried to correlate them with my fifteen years of physical misuse as a dentist – there's no question they are linked. The Alexander teacher gives me sympathy; it may not be part of the Alexander Technique but it helps.

I really wish I had known about the technique as a preventative. Dentists ought to be taught it as part of their training. It's tremendous, as it teaches you how not to misuse yourself. And it can make you feel so great and fit and right just by someone putting their hands on you. It gives you a tremendous 'high', you feel fit and alive and ready to go. I know my teacher can't produce normal vertebrae again, but she can make the best of what's there.

● *Joan, 54, housewife.* I had been written off by the medical profession. I had a slipped disc, which caused inflammation of the sciatic nerve, so I had excrutiating pain right down one leg. All they told me to do was go and lie down, and to stop doing all the things I normally do in running my home.

Well, I did that for three months. I also tried acupuncture and osteopathy and everything I could. Nothing would relieve this nerve. It just seemed to be trapped. Then I heard of the Alexander Technique, and I thought, well, I've got nothing to lose. So I had a few lessons with one teacher, who was good, then went over to my present one, who is really special. It does make a difference to believe in the person working on you.

I'm free from pain a lot of the time now, and I've been going to lessons for three years. The disc damaged the tissue, so I feel a dull ache at times, but the lessons have helped me to lengthen my spine up off it in the right way. Thinking 'up' is what really helps.

Things that have been tied up and tightened for years are beginning to release. Sometimes the lessons can cause pain and you feel different afterwards, but that can be good. I don't have the same feeling about pain as I did; it's not like something isn't ever going to go away; now I can deal with it by saying, well, it's bad this week but it's on its way out.

I've also changed in other ways. I'm taller and seem to have more length and width and a sense of well-being, so it's definitely not eyewash. One of the nicest things that has happened is that as I'm small, only 5′ 1″, I never had a neck. I felt my chin, collar and bust were all on top of one another. Now I can see my neck above my blouse collar.

It isn't till about six months into the lessons that it begins to open doors. It's both physical and mental; when your body is going well, you feel good. It comes from going 'up' instead of pulling down, like when you're crying you go all into a huddle, and most people never remember to straighten up again. It also makes you breathe. I don't know why, I just want to take deep breaths.

It's difficult to explain to someone who's never done it. You can't put your finger on exactly what makes it work. A lot of the Alexander Technique is thinking about what you're doing, and your body makes sense of it when you're doing things the right way. Most of the time people never give their bodies a thought, but when you suddenly stop and think, everything works so much better. The lessons have taught me to use the natural hinges we have. You rarely see people bend at the knees any more, it's always the back that's bent. So many people suffer with backs, I'm sure it could be avoided.

It doesn't take much time to think before you do things, though I'm the world's worst at remembering. I still rush around without thinking. But my teacher tells me I've been doing things this way for the last fifty years, so it's bound to take a bit of time. But you can change. I can't slump in a chair like I used to any more. And if I'm pushing myself too much, I spend fifteen minutes lying on my back on the floor, like they teach you, to relax.

If the Alexander Technique can do this much for me, with a problem, it must be marvellous for people who are O K to begin with.

Where to go

Society for the Teachers of the Alexander Technique
10 London House
266 Fulham Road
London SW10
Tel: 01-351-0828

BIODYNAMICS

What is it?

To biodynamic practitioners, the alimentary canal holds vital clues about our state of health and well-being. They maintain that as well as being a purely physical action in the digestive process, peristalsis – the churning movements of the intestines – is a delicate mechanism for processing our emotional intake, and reflects various degrees of tension left over from both the past and more recent upsets.

The therapist listens to the sounds of the peristalsis – our tummy rumblings – through a stethoscope. Using this as a diagnostic tool, she performs a gentle massage. The accompanying sounds, which can change from intermittent cracks to persistent gurglings, are thought to reflect directly the area of the body being treated. In fact, the more noise, the better, because this means that stress is being dissolved by the gut. Psychoperistalsis, as the stress-digesting is known, is a delicate feedback system intimately linked to energy flow in every part of the body.

The link between gut and stress

The idea that the body holds on to stress, which becomes manifested physically in a variety of ways, is central to all forms of bodywork. It is particularly relevant to biodynamic work because the therapy traces a clear, if somewhat esoteric, chain of events between emotional trauma and bodily reaction.

Many of us can accept the idea that we store tension, both physically imposed and the result of emotional pain: it is not difficult to understand how sitting in badly designed chairs has given us chronic backache or how shoulders have hunched in a defensive posture over the years. But how is this related to the innocent rumbling of a tummy? When you notice that emotional or traumatic moments are indeed accompanied by gurgling from the alimentary canal and that even mentally reliving past events can bring on tummy rumbles, it becomes easy to see the stomach as far more than a simple food processor. Says Mary Molloy, a biodynamic practitioner, 'It's important to remember that the alimentary canal and the tummy rumblings are not controlled by the conscious mind. They are part of a primitive system.'

This connection between tummy rumblings and your emotional state makes the biodynamic theory easier to understand, but there still remains the problem of how stress becomes translated into intestinal noise. Here there is little scientific or medical evidence, and one needs to have faith in the beliefs of the therapy's founder, Norwegian-born psychologist Gerda Boyesen.

Gerda Boyesen and the origins of biodynamics

Gerda Boyesen was born in Norway in 1920. Studying to be a clinical psychologist at Oslo University, she went through her own analysis with a Freudian who had been associated with Wilhelm Reich (see pp. 12–15). Although her therapist did not expound Reich's theories directly, Gerda Boyesen was influenced by them and became convinced of the importance of working with the body as an adjunct to verbal psychotherapy. As a result, she decided to qualify as a physiotherapist as well as a psychologist.

Boyesen studied the effects of neuro-muscular massage on psychiatric patients, and saw the dramatic changes these physical treatments had on the patients' psychological state. As a clinical psychologist in mental hospitals in Norway, she continued working on the relationship between psychological and physical processes. She was struck by what she called 'vegetative reactions' – flue, diarrhoea, changes in facial colour and loud tummy rumblings, especially at times of insight or emotional release. She also found that patients with these reactions improved more quickly than those whose physical state remained impassive.

Then she started to listen to her own intestinal sounds through a stethoscope, and the theory of psychoperistalsis was born. She found she could reduce excess fluid in her body tissue with massage and that this change brought about a sense of lightness and peace. Her starting point for explaining this change was Reich's theory of a universal life energy, which he also called 'orgone' energy or 'bioenergy' and which was based on Freud's theory of the libido. Reich said that when this energy flowed naturally, it was felt as a 'streaming' through the body. When this sensation was repressed, as usually hapens when we grow into 'socialized' beings, the movement of energy ceased accordingly, producing physical and psychological symptoms. The fully alive, spontaneous personality, which Boyesen called the primary personality, became overlaid by a secondary one full of doubts, fears and tensions.

Boyesen took this theory of energy movement and its interference a step further by defining an 'energetic fluid'. This is a fusion of two processes: the biological fluid systems of the body (blood, lymph, cerebro-spinal, interstitial, synovial) and the energy, a kind of electrical current that moves through the fluids. When the current of energy is stopped in any way, it becomes trapped or magnetically encapsulated with the fluid instead of travelling freely through it. We experience this as stress in its various forms, as a physical swelling at the site of this entrapment, a deadening of sensation, aches and pains or more serious degenerative disease.

Boyesen clarified three interconnected levels through which the life force flows: psychological, muscular and vegetative (which she defined as the basic life function governed by the nervous system). On this basis she decided that psychotherapy must go hand in hand with work directly on the body.

Her particular contribution was to study the vegetative level of experience and its relation to health and wholeness. Biodynamic massage is a physical release mechanism at the site of the trapped energy, freeing it from the fluid and enabling both to pursue their pathways unimpeded. Because this liberation is always accompanied by such insistent 'gut' reactions, Boyesen decided to give equal attention to this 'digestion' of the body's memory of the initial stressful experience. Psychoperistalsis is the biodynamic way of integrating and eventually eliminating this tension on all three levels.

In 1967 Gerda Boyesen established a centre in London. Her stated aim in biodynamic therapy is 'to regain access to the life force blocked in mind and body and to help it flow freely again through ingesting and assimilating repressed aspects of the self'.

What to expect

The first biodynamic massage is usually very gentle, calming and soothing. The therapist works to reassure the client, allowing her to feel safe about being touched and secure within the situation. She will also be particularly aware of when a patient is feeling nervous, fearful or is 'body armoured', with a lot of tension reflected in the posture. 'We have to build confidence so they realize physical therapy doesn't necessarily mean physical manipulation,' says Mary Molloy.

Even where a physical problem may have psychological causes obvious to the therapist, 'We would be misusing our knowledge if we went straight in and treated those causes without the patient's permission,' says Mary. The emphasis is on putting the patient at her ease and allowing tension to be released gradually and in its own time.

The patient is asked to lie on her back on the treatment couch. It is not usually necessary to undress. The stethoscope is placed just below the navel, on the right side of the abdomen over the area of the ileocaecal valve, which is where the small intestine enters the colon, or large intestine. Laying a reassuring hand on the patient's own hand or arm, the therapist inquires whether there is any pain or stiffness in the body, or any area that could do with special attention.

The first level of treatment is a 'palming massage', in which the surface of the skin over the muscles is just touched. More intense work on muscles may not come for several sessions; eventually the therapist aims to influence as deeply as bone level. All of this – skin, muscle and bone work – affects the nervous system and the more subtle energy systems.

At first just hands and arms are massaged, with the same light, stroking movements, feeling where energy is withheld. At the same time the therapist attunes herself to playback from the intestines. The patient can listen in too, as the sounds can be amplified, although some people prefer to lie quietly and use the session as a chance for complete relaxation. Sounds are remarkably different from area to area. They are easily distinguished from the normal digestion rumbles, by the trained therapist if not the patient. Sometimes there will be nothing to hear while a tense part is being massaged. Gradually the sound comes, at first dry

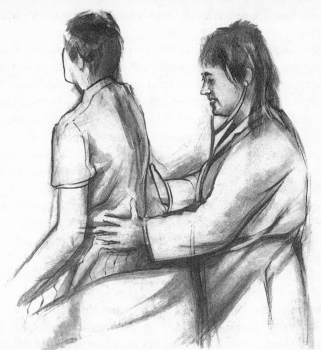

Biodynamic therapy is very gentle.

and crackling, then some larger 'thunderclaps', which signify the energy pathways opening up. When the sound becomes more continuous and less disjointed, things are really beginning to work. The therapist will massage each section for however long it takes to encourage this free flow and the accompanying noises that mean all is well.

At first only the smaller energy pathways are freed – those of the fingers and wrists, for example, stiff in most of us from constant use. The sensation is delicate and peaceful, with diagnosis and treatment going on simultaneously. In more advanced work the whole body receives attention. Reactions may be strong as underlying levels of tension are revealed and released. Usually after treatment a patient may need to visit the lavatory to eliminate released toxic waste products. Patients are also warned that in deeper work some nausea or diarrhoea may be experienced, although people vary in their reactions.

Sessions last one hour. Good results can be felt after just one massage, but this is really only a beginning, especially if there is any long-term problem. Weekly or fortnightly treatments over some months aim at gradual, safe release on psychological levels underlying the physical. While some patients may have emotional reactions during sessions, for many others benefits are just in feeling a new sense of optimism and resourcefulness in everyday life. Along with this release of trapped energy comes freedom from long-held pain.

Who benefits?

Anyone who senses their physical pain or distress may be linked to psychological causes or suffering from generalized anxiety and depression may wish to try biodynamic therapy. It has been effective in treating stress-related headaches, backache, arthritis, stomach and muscular aches and pains, and hypertension.

Biodynamic therapy is especially suited to those preferring a non-verbal approach. Little is demanded by way of participation other than to be open to receiving massage.

Personal view

● *Rosita, 39, teacher*. I found out about biodynamic work eight years ago when I had massage from a student who was learning it. I had had massage before, when

I was travelling in India and also from my grandmother in Mexico, but this was different. It was very simple but I felt clean and light afterwards, as if it affected all different areas.

Somehow when she treated one part, I would experience it somewhere else, as if a complete cleansing was taking place. I wasn't aware that I had anything wrong as such, but after that treatment I became interested and saved up for more. I came and had the massage regularly each week.

I found that physically my body was quite hot and that I had taut muscles and skin. I wasn't unhealthy, but my flexibility wasn't all that great.

The main point of the massage is the psychotherapy. As one progresses, the massage brings up emotional traumas and unfinished difficulties, also pleasure and joy that has been distorted. I come from a strict upbringing and according to Gerda Boyesen's theory I was a 'rigid' type, not at its most exaggerated but physically and in my attitude. The treatments uncovered relationships in my family which had all affected me. Lots of things started coming up about my religious, moral and racial values, all the result of my mixed Spanish/Indian cultural background. So I could start to understand myself through the treatment. It really cleaned through the surface and went into much deeper levels.

I've been going regularly once a week, with a few breaks in between. I also became aware I had been suffering from constipation, and the treatments had the effect of regulating my bowel movements. Physically, too, the tone of my skin has improved and my muscles have become more flexible. Now the treatments affect my body and psyche as much as each other, and I feel my whole well-being is improved. It's as if my body is

more centred, and I don't have to make demands on
anyone else. I can just be there as myself.

Where to go

Gerda Boyesen Institute
Acacia House
Centre Avenue
London W3
Tel: 01-743-2437

BIOENERGETICS

What is it?

Bioenergetics is a technique to help integrate emotions fully with the body. It sees the human body as a vital means of emotional expression, which we mostly abandon as we grow up and learn to deal with intense feelings in all sorts of distorted ways.

As babies and small children, until controlled by parents, teachers and the social and cultural environment, we have many direct, physical ways of expressing our emotions. We all can remember times when we screamed with rage, shook with fear, kicked out in anger, vomited up undesired food or reached out to a parent in a moment of pleasure. We recognize this behaviour in children and often, reminded of our own painful emotions when confronted with their tears, try to ease them out of such ways of expressing themselves.

As adults, our main pathway to expressing strong feelings, whether painful or joyous, is through the mind. Once the lessons of growing up are impressed on us, allowing an emotion to have its physical release is a thing of the past. So whenever we feel angry, or in need or even, on many occasions, loving, we send the feeling straight to the intellect. There it is considered and the correct mental and verbal expressions formulated.

This is all very 'civilized', but the harm it does to our being is evident. It can be seen posturally. Shoulders stick defensively in a position of fear, when they should have shaken it off. Arms may be weak and easily tired through years of rigidly controlling their desire to reach out to others. A hunch in the upper back, according to bioenergetic theory, is usually the result of withheld anger. When an animal is angry the hair stands up along its spine and its back arches. When adults consistently hold back that feeling instead of allowing it full progression along the back and into the arms and head, they may experience tension and pain, which eventually may develop into so-called dowager's hump or hunchback.

The voice may be thin and weak, not properly reflecting what we want to say. Breathing may not flow regularly and the body can look 'cut off' or divided at various levels – for instance, top heavy or with most of the energy or movement evident at the head and shoulder level. We may experience sexual difficulties or have a variety of physical health problems. Self-expression and creativity may be restricted, as we sense there is much more we 'could' do, yet lack the means to do it.

Feelings and energy

Some of these may sound like heavy-duty ills to be laid at the door of emotion. To link them, it is important to understand the relationship between emotion and energy. It is easy to see how it works: imagine going to meet someone you love, from whom you have been separated for a long time. You have to pick him or her up at the airport at an unearthly hour of the morning. Is it hard to get up and go? Far from it, you will hardly sleep, and be up before time. The energy is there, created by the emotions.

Contrast that scenario with waking up on a rainy Friday on which you have a meeting scheduled with a particularly ill-tempered boss. How is the energy level that morning? Do you leap out of bed smiling? No, it's far more likely that you feel tired and drained. If the meeting goes badly, you may well have developed physical aches and pains by that evening.

So our most primary feelings have a direct action line to our energy levels, and this energy affects every part of our being. Where it becomes held up, or blocked, depends greatly on the nature of the basic emotion and its pattern of expression in the body. Its form of manifestation will depend on the genetic disposition of the individual, although to what extent our emotional inheritance predisposes us to family patterns of illness continues to be the subject of much argument.

Bioenergetics aims to create an integration between body and emotions. The ideal is for an emotion and its natural physical discharge to take place simultaneously. When that occurs, there is no build-up of the energy charge and no physical traces of suppression. Bioenergetic work also aims to unlock the repressed areas of the past and create the means to release long-held feelings that may be preventing a fully alive energy flow. In the words of Alexander Lowen, the therapy's originator, 'Bioenergetics is a therapeutic technique to help a person get back together with his body and to help him enjoy to the fullest degree possible the life of the body. The emphasis on the body includes sexuality, which is one of its basic functions. But it also includes the even more basic functions of breathing, moving, feeling and self-expression.' If any of these is not free, said Lowen, the life of the body is restricted and we live in fear of being fully alive.

Alexander Lowen and the origins of bioenergetics

Alexander Lowen, the patriarch of bioenergetics, was born in America at the turn of the century and now lives in California. His interest in the relationship between body and mind began in the 1930s, when he was an athletics director at a summer camp. He noticed that improving his physical health did the same for his mental state and thus became convinced that mental attitudes could be affected by working on the body.

After attending a lecture by Wilhelm Reich (see pp. 12–15) Lowen became interested in Reich's theories about the energy charge attached to the repression of feelings, its build-up, conversion into physical reality and the possibility of discharge in the body.

Lowen had therapy with Reich from 1942 until 1945. He thought he had no particular problems, but in the first session, Reich pointed out that Lowen's chest was barely moving as he breathed. On Reich's instructions Lowen moved his head back and an involuntary scream, totally unexpected and not unpleasant, was released. He saw then that 'I was not as all right as I thought. There were things in my personality that were hidden from consciousness, and I knew then that they would have to come out.'

Lowen found that, gradually, through breathing freely and allowing his body to move, he experienced spontaneous energy changes. Cramp, tingling and tremors were accompanied by sudden memories from childhood. He began to be able to cry and to express feelings in a new way, and at the same time his breathing became deeper and less restricted. Later he began to work with patients himself, as a Reichian therapist.

From 1947 until 1951 Lowen studied medicine at Geneva in Switzerland, and received his degree as a doctor of medicine. At the same time, he continued his Reichian work, although he was becoming increasingly isolated from Reich and his followers and more and more interested in developing the body-focused approach. With a colleague, John Pierrakos, Lowen began to develop positions and exercises using the whole body to release muscular tension. During the three years they worked together, he found it became easier to surrender to his feelings instead of trying to be in control. When the association with Pierrakos ended, Lowen continued to use the bioenergetic exercises they had evolved and to work with patients and in groups.

Lowen says, 'If someone asked me [when the therapy with Pierrakos ended] "Have you resolved all your problems, completed your growth, realized your full potential as a person or released all your muscular tensions?" my answer would still have been "no".' He simply felt at this point that he was able to take on the full responsibility for his well-being and continued development. The changes that occurred thereafter were a result of his commitment to working with his body, in conjunction with a deeper understanding of himself and his past history.

One of Lowen's important discoveries was the need to become more 'grounded', that is, to bring energy to the legs and feet in order to feel more in touch with reality. Lowen found all his patients lacked a sense of 'having their feet planted firmly on the floor', and he equated this downward pull of energy to becoming reacquainted with very basic feelings, including sexuality, and getting away from illusion and fantasy. That is, it became an essential part of becoming solid and well-balanced.

His basic exercise to encourage this was the arch or bow (also known as the fundamental stress position). It entails placing the fists at the small of the back, bending the knees and arching backwards with the legs apart and the toes turned inwards. The entire body is in an arc or bow shape, with the centre point between the shoulders directly above that of the feet. The legs gradually begin to vibrate with the energetic charge of the position.

Lowen says the body is perfectly balanced in this shape (which is also an ancient Chinese Taoist exercise aimed at attaining harmony with the universe). However, such a seemingly simple position presents several problems. Many

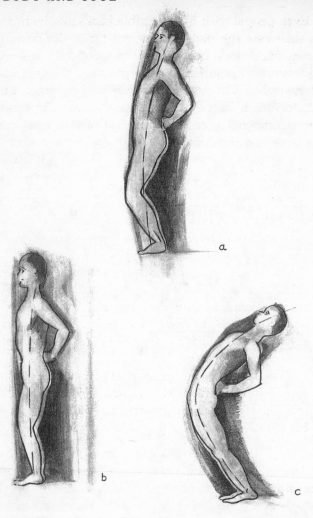

The bow, done correctly (a) and incorrectly (b) and (c).

people are so rigid that they cannot arch properly. Legs and ankles are often particularly inflexible. The lower back may also be tense and the pelvis immovable.

Even people with hyperflexible backs can be in trouble. In their case the body is bent too far in the bow and the lower back does not support it properly. Instead, the abdominal muscles become contracted through carrying that weight. While the rigid body goes with an inflexible temperament, over-flexibility, says Lowen, is a clue to a personality that is too weak and pliable. Lowen sums up his work and his philosophy thus:

Since the living body includes the mind, the spirit and the soul, to live the life of the body fully is to be mindful, spiritual and soulful. If we are deficient in these aspects of our being, it is because we are not fully in or with our bodies. We treat the body as an instrument or machine. We know that if it breaks down, we are in trouble. But the same could be said of the automobile on which we so much depend. We are not identified with our body; in fact, we have betrayed it. All our personal difficulties stem from this betrayal and I believe that most of our social problems have a similar origin.

The goal of bioenergetics is to help people regain their primary nature, which is the condition of being free, the state of being graceful and the quality of being beautiful. They denote a healthy body and also, therefore, a healthy mind.

Lowen's conclusion is: 'The life of an individual is the life of the body.'

What to expect

Bioenergetics is powerful, perhaps one of the most powerful of all the physical therapies. It also, therefore, carries certain dangers and its mention is sometimes accompanied by suspicion and warnings. One bioenergetic therapist explains it this way: 'It is a marvellous map and a way of understanding people. But it is like a scalpel – it can cut deeply. In the hands of a surgeon the scalpel can be extremely effective. But it can be misused.'

The bioenergetic exercises can release very strong emotions suddenly, as in Lowen's first experience with Reich. Obviously this can be a shock to the system, especially if the emotions are linked to deep traumas from the past whose memory was checked precisely because they were so agonizing. The release can bring a great deal of pain and distress, and it takes a proficient therapist to deal with such possibilities.

There are three main ways to work with bioenergetics. One is in private sessions with a therapist. This can be intense. The client is helped by means of probing questions to focus on her emotions, then encouraged to express them in terms of sobbing, sighing, crying, roaring or whatever fits. After a while questioning becomes unnecessary: clients learn instantaneous expression and there is much more access to personal history and relationships. Any conflicts between how to express oneself emotionally and the fear of self-expression will then be open to discussion.

A bioenergetic movement group is different but complementary. The therapist gives a set of bioenergetic exercises designed to move energy and which may cause emotional expression. The bow exercise (see pp. 67–8) is one of the mainstays of a bioenergetic movement class. The other exercises might include some of Lowen's original ones, but many are devised by individual therapists working within the bioenergetic framework. There is no set series of exercises in bioenergetic work, and the groups vary tremendously according to the therapist in charge. Perhaps the one thing they have in common is that they are all, as the name suggests, highly physically energetic, since the approach is designed to disturb the suppressed emotions held within the energy system.

After such physical work has been completed, there will be 'voicing' work, such as repeating your name to each member of the group, sometimes loudly, sometimes quietly. This vocalizing is important: it allows your own sound to come through and join the active physical processes, and can shake loose a lot of withheld feelings. Then there is an opportunity for 'letting rip' with the voice in more emotionally-charged exercises or performing reaching-out movements and accompanying them with any sounds or words that come forth spontaneously. Such work can be highly self-revealing, but in the context of a group there is less self-consciousness and the joint effort creates an atmosphere in which you can participate without feeling foolish. Groups end with a quiet time when everyone can relax and talk about what has happened if they wish. There is no intimidation or compulsion during a session; how much you do is up to you. It is perfectly possible to take part in the group for the aerobic exercise experience alone – it will still be beneficial.

The movement class usually lasts around two hours. People tend to go for a year or two, then move on to other forms of therapy or incorporate bioenergetic work with something else. Definite benefits can be felt within about a dozen sessions, going on a weekly basis.

The third way to work with bioenergetics is to do the exercises alone, at home, after you have attained a certain level of familiarity with them. But such a regime should be accompanied by other therapy to deal with any discoveries that may result from this individual practice. One-to-one and individual bioenergetic therapy are not necessarily accompanied by group work, but it is a useful back-up.

Who benefits?

Therapist Guy Gladstone, who leads regular groups in London, thinks bioenergetics can help most people who feel somewhat 'locked up' emotionally and/or physically – 'normal neurotic people' – to obtain better overall expression. Those with some degree of bodily rigidity do best, Gladstone says, especially within the group, where there is not so much individual exposure as in the personal therapy relationship. These are the people who get the most, soonest, in terms of a change in emotional functioning. However, he explains, since the movement group work is rather forceful and demands a certain amount of self- responsibility, activity and commitment, it is not appropriate for everyone.

The strenuous physical work-out in the movement class is contra-indicated for anyone with high blood pressure. People with very serious problems and those who are very timid should not attend a bioenergetic movement group, at least not initially. They are better trying individual therapy first, which can proceed at the client's own pace, although any form of bioenergetic therapy may be too strong for people unused to working on an emotional level.

Personal views

● *Frank, 33, personnel officer.* My feelings about myself came to a head when I applied for a promotion at work and didn't get it. Instead it went to a person I didn't respect in any way. I went for counselling and bioenergetics was suggested to me. I've only been eight times, but it's been tremendous. I don't know what stress is any more.

At work I feel I'm where I always wanted to be. Physically, I move with more ease, and am getting on so much better with people. My work performance has improved and is being recognized at high levels. In fact, a lot of people can see the difference in me.

I've always tended to look at people analytically and to feel removed from them. Now my sensitivity to people has really improved. It's difficult when you've been brought up in industrial relations, as I have; you're taught a very confrontational attitude, not to be understanding and sympathetic.

I'm feeling my way through things far more instead of relying on my analytical, logical ability. I trust my own judgement. For instance, the last time I wrote a report, I gave it in the first time and it was accepted. Normally I'd have had to do it over and over again, I'd never have trusted myself to leave it at the first attempt. It's like having dived from a diving board. For the first time I can trust that my gut reactions are right.

I've always felt quite creative but not known how to express it. In sessions sometimes visions come up, mythological figures and that kind of thing. I also find my hearing is more acute afterwards, when I listen to the car stereo on the way home. I feel quite excited by all this. I'm discovering myself and I don't know where it will end. I don't understand it, but it's very encouraging. I feel that things will work out. I'll certainly carry on with the class.

● *Ian, 42, business manager.* During the movement class I had an experience of something which I didn't know was there and hadn't been able to get in touch with any other way. It was during a session of foot stamping – I had a sudden personal sense of power. It seemed to switch on like an electric current, almost like magic. I just felt I knew exactly what to do.

It's an experience that's difficult to convey, but it meant I didn't have to depend on others or manipulate them to get what I wanted. I haven't consciously used this feeling since, or been able to re-access it in ordinary life, so it's hard to assess its relevance. But having experienced it was of enormous importance and gave me a new perspective on myself.

Where to go

British Institute for
Bioenergetic Analysis
c/o Gerald Peck
17 York Villas
Brighton BN1 3TS
Tel: 0273-729724

Scottish Centre for
Bioenergetic Analysis
c/o Dr David Campbell
The Davidson Clinic
Charing Cross Mansions
12 St George's Road
Glasgow G3 6UJ
Tel: 041-332-6371

Guy Gladstone
The Open Centre
188 Old Street
London EC1
Tel: 01-254-8047,
01-549-9583

John Andrew Miller
22 Fitzjohn's Avenue
London NW3 5NB
Tel: 01-435-1079

DANCE

THERAPY

Long before dance became a performing art, with structure and form dictated by country and culture, it was one of the most powerful rituals of ancient societies. Stylized movement was an accepted way of expressing strong personal feelings, such as anger, happiness and fear, and of transforming their fundamental energy into creative forces. The early religious rituals in which the ecstasy or even trance-like state induced by the dance resulted in loosening inhibitions and a release from everyday anxieties and conflicts – a kind of personal purging – were perhaps the first forms of dance therapy. Today dance therapy is based on studies of both group ritual dance and the dance of tribal medicine men, or shamans, and incorporates their ancient methods of inducing harmony of mind and body.

The principal components of dance – rhythm and movement – can help people to express non-verbally what is happening deep within themselves and to reharmonize themselves at many different levels. It is a way for anyone to explore the self more thoroughly. It can also free people from physical ailments engendered by the stress of holding the body in rigid positions. In so doing, it can help to re-educate the body. By noting how the individual dances, an experienced therapist sees where tensions are held and can encourage more harmonious movement.

The origins of dance therapy

Dance therapy can be said to have been inspired by the work of Rudolph Laban (1879–1958), whose chief fame lies in introducing modern dance to Europe and in the system of dance notation that bears his name. Laban was interested in analysing and communicating how individuals move, in particular their orientation in the surrounding space, and the contrasting dynamics that colour everyday movement and mood: the qualities of strong and delicate, direct and indirect, staccato and legato, and the use of acceleration and deceleration as movement flows. Laban saw movement as a harmonizing experience, and therefore therapeutic in its own right. He was involved in therapeutic and educational work in England after fleeing Germany at the outbreak of the Second World War, but he did not specialize in dance therapy.

It was in America in the 1950s that dance therapy really began. This was the time when modern, or contemporary, dance was becoming popular. Improvisation, a freer style of movement and greater rhythmic variations were part of the reaction against the constraints of classical ballet. The therapeutic use of dance was developed largely through the efforts of two creative dance teachers. Mary Whitehouse began to link the way her dance students moved with the inner feelings they expressed. Applying her knowledge of Jungian psychology to movement, she gradually attracted non-dancers to her classes purely for the therapeutic insights they received there.

Also working in America at that time was Marian Chace, who taught creative, inspirational dance, by its very nature directed towards personal expression. Impressed by the therapeutic value of her classes, psychiatrists at a nearby hospital started sending their patients to her. Later, they invited her to work in the hospital with patients whose psychological problems were considered too severe for them to mix with other people. Chace noted that patients' feelings of isolation and not being understood were significantly reduced by the opportunity for expression they achieved through dance. She promoted the use of dance as a basic communication method, saying it 'offers the individual a means of relating himself to the environment when he is cut off in the majority of areas by the patterns of his illness'.

Other innovative teachers followed, all working along lines influenced by their individual fields of interest. Trudi Schoop used improvisational development, while Liljan Espenak integrated dance with Adlerian depth psychotherapy for mentally retarded and other functionally disabled people. In Britain Gina Levete has been important in organizing dance therapy for the disabled.

What to expect

Dance therapists vary widely in their background and approach. Some have a classical dance training, while others have studied different forms of expressive movement. Some apply the theories of Jung, others prefer Freud and many use humanistic psychologies such as *Gestalt*. Laban therapists tend to look at a client's present movement in terms of how the various physical processes of growing up – sitting up, reaching out, taking the first steps – were managed. Ultimately, a dance therapist uses the sum total of her own activities and personal exploration to provide a unique integration of dance and psychology.

Dance therapy for the person who functions normally but feels the need to explore unsatisfactory aspects of behaviour takes place in one-to-one sessions or groups. While the sessions can help the individual face problems quickly,

groups focus on patterns in communication and are therefore useful for revealing how one reacts to others.

Usually, a therapist working with an individual first just
watches how the client walks round the room; movement
betrays what the client herself barely knows. The therapist
will notice where the body's energy flows naturally and
well, and where there are problems, as shown by jerky or
uncoordinated movement patterns or disconnection between breathing and posture. Without needing an explana-
tion, the trained therapist sees what lies hidden behind
each physical expression.

Methods vary, but the intention always is to free trapped
energy and improve the individual's ability to explore self-
expressive movement. If a client habitually avoids, or finds
difficult, wide, reaching-out movements, the therapist may
deliberately introduce them into a sequence. Once they
become familiar and not so frightening, the individual
begins to sense the kind of feelings that accompany the
movement. The therapist's job is to help her experience
every kind of movement, in a variety of sequences that are
not imposed but evolve from the client, thus becoming her
own 'dance'.

Musical instruments are often used. For example, a client
may be asked to stamp to a drum or a tambourine. With
some people this movement may be tentative, displaying
their difficulty in assertiveness, or it may uncover stored
aggression. Whatever happens, it is a comfortable way of
getting the responses out and seeing them through a different medium to that of thought and verbalization. Some
therapists like to discuss the client's experience but it is by
no means obligatory; this is essentially a non-rationalizing
therapy. The primary experience is always through the
movement, and the sensations are displayed through the
body, not the mind.

The most profound experience in a session is the sense of

touching and exploring uncharted areas. We are used to making habitual movements repeatedly. By widening our physical expression we gain access to much that is untapped inside ourselves and can learn to use it more effectively. After a number of sessions, people find they are using a far wider range of movement than before. Says therapist Gay Parker, 'As children we run, jump and leap around. But as we get older our usual movement possibilities become more limited, and we have to hold in feeling with the movement. We don't usually get the opportunity to continue to express ourselves in movement, and dance therapy gives some of this back.'

Paradoxically, dance therapy is not always much to do with dance. You will not be taught a performance technique nor end up able to do a dance routine. True, harmony is paramount, but the movements employed are more often fundamental ones of rocking, stamping, stretching and lifting, than specific dance steps. The concept of dance as a personal expression and form of emotional catharsis is far more important than its performance potential.

However, work towards a performance is occasionally useful. 'An actual performance of creative dance can be very therapeutic,' says Gay Parker. 'Using dance to help develop self-awareness or making it into an art form really both overlap.' Mentally handicapped people, in particular, benefit from the group effort of performance.

In personal therapy, a series of classes is recommended, and sometimes therapists give exercises to do at home. These may be similar to general fitness exercises and may also incorporate breathing exercises. Dance is a long-term therapy; even though a single session shows areas on which a client needs to work, practising a new way of being takes time.

Group classes often differ by being one-off day or week-end events. They also use music to encourage self-

For many people dance therapy is the first time they have moved without inhibition since childhood.

expression and work with rhythm, mood and personal contact.

Who benefits?

Dance therapy can help people who find it difficult to talk about themselves to become more fully alive, healthy and expressive. For them the body can say much more and give access to greater depths of emotion than words alone. A dance therapist is able to spot where a person is physically or emotionally blocked by the way the parts of the body move and by the rhythms created.

Dance therapy is also used to great effect with people who are severely mentally handicapped, many of whom find it inhibiting to move at all. The therapist can give such people the impetus to experience the body, perhaps for the first time in a long while. Many patients build up a new sense of self-confidence and from that are able to use imagery – for instance, moving as if rocked by the sea – to express themselves in simple movements.

Other forms of movement therapy

Dancercise

Created by dancer and journalist Phyllis Greene Morgan, Dancercise is 'dance for non-dancers'. She says, 'Dance is too marvellous to be left to the professional dancer. As exercise, it is one of the most thorough and effective, and it gives immediate results that last a lifetime. As a recreation, dance brings pleasure and release.'

Dancercise incorporates different dance techniques and training exercises. Each class gives a thorough workout, and over a few terms can reform the body and the way of moving. Because the teachers are professional dancers, classes are very safe – and fun. People of all ages and degrees of fitness can benefit.

Eurhythmy

Eurhythmy was created by the Austrian spiritual philosopher Rudolph Steiner. Its aim is to express in movement and gesture the sounds used in speech and music. Their intrinsic power can be captured and expressed in particular by hand and arm movement, Steiner found, for these are the means of natural gesture that accompany the sounds people make. In eurhythmy, however, movement is not confined here, but is reflected by the entire body. 'In a performance of eurhythmy,' say the London School of Eurhythmy, 'the body should be seen as clothed by the movement inherent in the sound.'

Performances bring to life a poem or piece of music through movement that seems more than just physical. Eurhythmy students feel their arms and legs, feet, hands and head begin, as it were, to speak and to sing; the whole organism becomes an instrument of speech and music. Eurhythmists also work with sick people and can help them confront and deal with their illness.

Natural dance

As the name implies, in this form of dance people experiment with and explore the movements that arise spontaneously when they respond creatively to rhythm. It is based on dance, or 'contact', improvisation, which is the way dancers relate to each other on stage. Though often geared to performance work, many classes are now available to the less experienced as well as complete newcomers, and children – all those who want to dance for fun and to enjoy the natural movement of the body.

Much of this work has been influenced by Anna Halprin, who teaches in San Francisco, using ethnic dance forms from Africa and Arabia, for example, and involves the community rather than just dancers. She aims to enhance creativity and self-knowledge through returning to the natural expression of movement without imposed technique.

Personal views

● *Angela, 27, estate agent.* I came to dance therapy because I have always been interested in dance and movement. I had always liked to dance but had become very sedentary in recent years. This seemed like an opportunity to move around again and have some insight into myself at the same time.

The first session was a mixture of free association dancing, yoga, exercise and relaxation. I just had to move around and 'explore the space' in my normal way, while my therapist noticed things about the way I walked and where I was tense. Then we did some work with specific dance actions. I had to find different ways of using my hands in space. Although at first it seemed very boring, soon the movement just took over and my hands found a rhythm of their own. That was quite fascinating and I really forgot myself in this movement and created my own dance.

Then she gave me some pure exercises, which I have to do every day at home, to strengthen my legs where the therapist saw there was tension and also to free the locked energy around my hips. These are very simple and don't take long, and I find them helpful.

We also did some work to music. Some people need more music, throughout a session, if they are perhaps inhibited about moving around without any sound. It felt a bit strange at first, moving with someone looking at you, but once you get used to the therapist you soon get over any self-consciousness.

My therapist also banged on a drum and I had to stamp to it; that made me feel very positive and confident. Perhaps the most useful exercise we did was where I had to create my own rhythm. I found myself working out a very complicated one, and trying to move to it not very successfully. It was hard for my therapist to feel what the rhythm was, too. From this she asked me some very leading questions: was my life rather complicated with a lot of varied tasks that I wasn't dealing with very well? That was spot on and we talked about this briefly, but it was enough that it had come to my attention.

I feel after six weekly sessions that my body has become stronger and I am more integrated. I have learned that one problem area was my breathing – it was very shallow and this often led to my feeling tired and confused. The dance movements somehow opened my lungs and made me breathe more deeply and evenly. I realized I often had to gasp for breath before. I definitely feel I move more harmoniously and without so much tension, and am more aware of myself as a rhythmic, 'whole' person. I also feel my approach to life is easier and not so unnecessarily complicated.

● *Susan, 54, housewife*. I was attending a clinic after suffering bouts of suicidal depression. The first time we had dance therapy, I was very unresponsive and just sat next to the wall, but then the therapist came and sat beside me and mirrored my position. That had an immediate effect; I felt I had real contact with someone for the first time for a long while.

We had the same therapist twice a week and I began

to feel a new sense of trust and wanted to join in. We did a lot of relaxation and some exercises that made us aware of different parts of the body so they began to feel more alive; I had never done anything like it before.

Then one day came a real breakthrough for me. We were doing some stamping movements to music and mine became stronger and louder till I was shouting, I was almost beside myself. I recognized that I was furious at my father and my former husband and suddenly I knew that I had been directing all that at myself. I felt so released and free afterwards, I'll never forget that moment. It was the beginning of my recovery. I stopped taking the medication I was on and found myself able to talk normally to other people again instead of just in monosyllables.

I wouldn't say this kind of therapy would solve all the problems of many other people like me, but in my case it was wonderfully successful – at least it has been so far, six years on.

Where to go

The Association for Dance
Movement Therapy
99 South Hill Park
London NW3 2SP
Tel: 01-794-9833

Laban Guild
c/o Anna Carlisle
7 St Anne's Crescent
Lewes, Sussex
Tel: 0273-476335

Dancercise
The Barge Durban
Lion Wharf
Richmond Road
Old Isleworth,
Middlesex TW7 7BW
Tel: 01-560-3300,
027-976-640

London School of
Eurhythmy
Dunnings Road
East Grinstead, RH19 4NF
Tel: 0342-312527

Chisenhale Dance Space
64–84 Chisenhale Road
London E3
Tel: 01-981-6617,
01-980-8115

FELDENKRAIS

METHOD

What is it?

Feldenkrais is a method of learning about physical function and use of the self, and works towards improving the quality of movement in everything you do. The method does not teach one particular way of moving as being better than any other. Rather, it gives the chance to experience different ways of using the body, so the student can find out for himself if there is a more simple, economical and easy way of doing things than he has been accustomed to. The movement is not discussed or analysed, but is a quiet, personal experience. Once felt for oneself, it can be more easily incorporated into daily life.

People learn to move as they grow, through a process of education. In fact, we humans are rare in having very few of our movement patterns programmed into our nervous system. It is a relatively long time before a human baby can walk on its own, especially compared with most other mammals, which are up and running within hours of birth. Whether it is rocking, sitting, talking, rolling over, crawling, playing football or ballet dancing, all are essentially learned movement patterns.

We learn movements in a variety of ways. As children we spend much of our time moving, exploring, playing and getting feedback on our actions. When you look around, you see that everyone has learned differently, according to their own experience and training. Whether we learned efficiently or not is another matter. Like most other things that depends on the kind of training we received and, in regard to the fundamentals of sitting up, standing and walking, especially on our role models.

There is, however, another form of education, according to Moshe Feldenkrais, the originator of the method: self-education. Self-education occurs when we grow and become more stable, and instead of just absorbing the environment, develop individual characteristics and begin to make choices. While 'imposed education and individual propensities together set the trend for all our habitual movement action', when we begin self-education we no longer accept everything that our training tries to impose on us. At this stage there is a possibility for change.

Disappointingly, observed Feldenkrais, the active, individual force of self-education is also open to misuse. Most people try to fit into society and therefore, 'every aspiration and spontaneous desire is subjected to stringent internal criticism lest they reveal the individual's organic nature.' Since we are afraid of self-exposure, he maintains, we lie behind a mask of personality that we try to present to others and even use to fool ourselves. Thus even personal choice confronts us with the conflict of whether to conform and be accepted, or to follow our own instincts and risk being ostracized. Not only does this impose mental stress, it may also create structural and functional conflicts, such as disturbances in digestion, elimination, breathing or bone structure. Even when these improve, the respite may be only temporary, followed by another decrease in vitality and well-being.

Nevertheless, we can also choose to re-educate ourselves in a beneficial manner, instead of continuing on this sort of spiral of depletion, Feldenkrais suggested. However, he made clear that it is not a choice for the cowardly or the impatient. It is:

hard and complicated, but for every person who feels the need for change and improvement it is within the limits of practical possibility. It must be fully realized from the start that the learning process is irregular and consists of steps, and that there will be downs as well as ups. It should further be realized that as changes take place in the self, new and hitherto unrecognized difficulties will be discovered. It is only as self-confidence increases that it becomes possible to identify them. As people try to better themselves, different stages of development can be found in each of them.

The Feldenkrais method is not geared towards emotional self-expression or any kind of cathartic experience, but concentrates on working with the physical body and through its movement increasing awareness of all aspects of our being. This is not to say Feldenkrais denied the relationship between emotions and physiology. Indeed, he had much to say about the impact of emotional disturbance on the way we look and move, and particularly on the effects of carrying round an anxiety state. Through changing our mode of using the body, through making more appropriate choices, he believed that change was possible throughout the whole organism.

Moshe Feldenkrais and the origins of the method

Moshe Feldenkrais was a Jew born on the border of Russia and Poland in 1904. He emigrated to what was then Palestine around the time of the First World War, and worked as a labourer. His main interest was self-defence. Gradually, through study and interpretation of various Oriental martial arts techniques, he developed his own system, which he taught to the small Jewish population in Palestine.

After the war Feldenkrais gained entry to the Sorbonne in Paris to study physics. He received his doctorate of science and subsequently worked with Fredrick Joliot-Curie in his laboratory. Throughout this period he maintained his interest in martial arts, and published his first book on the subject. The book was to prove the key to the highest martial arts circles. Arriving uninvited at an important exhibition of self-defence techniques, where admission was by special ticket only, Moshe Feldenkrais presented a copy of his book. The result was not only entry, but an invitation to a special reception, at which he was introduced to the top martial arts exponents in Paris and succeeded in impressing them with his self-taught techniques. Under their wing he began more directed training, which earned him a black belt in traditional judo, and helped set up the French judo association.

When the Second World War came, Feldenkrais fled to Britain, where he worked for the Ministry of Defence developing anti-submarine techniques. Anyone who knew him then, though, was struck more by his passion for judo than his military work. He led an active physical life, teaching self-defence and playing soccer. The result of his somewhat over-enthusiasm was a number of injuries, including a damaged knee, which worsened with time.

Encountering medical pessimism about his condition, he determined to find a cure himself. He began to explore how he moved, what caused pain and what exacerbated it. Feldenkrais spent the years just after the war methodically researching anatomy, physiology, neuro-physiology and kinesiology, trying to find out what he had done. His scientific background orientated him towards trying to formulate principles that worked, then experimenting until precise answers were found. Looking at the problems of other sufferers who came to him for help added a practical dimension to his research. He developed a complete concept about movement, in terms of habit, function, and the relationship to gravity. These ideas were expressed in his book *Body and Mature Behaviour*, published in 1949. So far, though, he was concerned only with evolving ideas, there was nothing directly experiential about his work.

At this time Feldenkrais met F. Matthias Alexander (see pp. 43–53) and attended his classes with great interest, finding that Alexander's ideas corresponded very much with his own. Both men had arrived independently at the concept of inhibiting habitual movements and replacing them with movements that worked better. However, Alexander was rather protective of his work, afraid lest Feldenkrais steal his ideas, and so the two men went their separate ways. Alexander was ultimately more of an idealist and visionary, Feldenkrais a scientist.

Feldenkrais continued with his research, travelling all over Europe and meeting the chief personalities involved in movement education techniques. In the 1950s he moved back to what had become Israel, and settled in Tel Aviv, his base for the rest of his life. Here he worked, researched, gave lessons and classes and, in the 1960s, began to develop an apprenticeship system with his followers.

During the late 1960s Feldenkrais became known further abroad, and was invited to teach at the Esalen Institute in California. Esalen was *the* place for innovative philosophies, therapies and all forms of new and holistic treatment, a hive of inspiration, with leaders of the human potential movement gathering from far and near. The exposure to the United States was very exciting for Feldenkrais, leading to fresh experiment and exploration. Many people came to listen to him and attend his classes. As his popularity grew, a training for Feldenkrais teachers was organized in the United States.

Moshe Feldenkrais died in 1984. His method is popular throughout Europe and in Australia and the United States.

What to expect

In individual work, called Functional Integration, the therapist puts his hands on the client and guides him into subtle new ways of using his body. Feldenkrais teacher Christopher Connolly says, 'My hands are educated so I could take the student through different movement patterns in a way that is non-threatening, efficient and which honours the integrity of the body.' Lessons are approximately forty-five minutes long.

Awareness through Movement is the name given to group work. Groups can last for an hour and a half and take place on a regular basis, or be concentrated into day or weekend workshops.

Both are effective but the individual work tends to show quicker results since students are taken through specific movements directly geared to their own physical blocks and limitations.

A Feldenkrais lesson is very gentle. Moshe Feldenkrais felt that a state of excitation wasn't conducive to learning. The higher the arousal level, he believed, the more likely a person is to resort to previously learned behaviour and act on pure reflex. In a calm, relaxed atmosphere, there is a greater degree of control over the motor cortex of the brain, and thought processes can direct movement more effectively.

The Feldenkrais Method involves hundreds of movements, some small and some larger. They can be put together in any number and sequence the teacher decides. The general intention is always the same: to increase awareness, interrupt habitual behaviour and gain control over the central nervous system, which, in turn, informs muscular-skeletal motion.

Many of the movements are done lying down. Feldenkrais maintained it was very difficult to change deep-seated movement patterns when standing because too many actions are involved in order to keep a person upright against the force of gravity. Lying or sitting, one can discover what it is like to move without the additional battle against falling over.

The type of session depends on the envisaged goal. If, for example, it is stress reduction, Christopher Connolly explains, he might spend a whole lesson on the eye area, erasing accumulated stress. He would get the student to raise her eyebrows by herself, then using her hand. Next he could ask her to move the eyebrows out to one side, then integrate that movement with the eyes, and then differentiate the action of the eyes from that of brows by moving the eyebrows up and the eyes down, and so on. Then, when normal movement is resumed, it is with greater awareness of its totality.

The lesson might continue with breathing, circling eyebrows and eyes, gradually opening out and expanding the awareness. 'Then I can begin to look at what the student is doing with his breathing, when the jaw is held tight, what happens at the back of the neck, and bring all that into the awareness of the body so all the habits and tensions held in the eyebrows are released,' explains Christopher Connolly.

Another favourite lesson is the 'pelvic clock'. Lying down, the student imagines a clock beneath the pelvis and begins to tilt towards 9 o'clock, 12, 3 and so on. This extremely gentle rotation and twisting discovers all the new areas the body can touch on. The same circling can be done with the clock face at the back of the head, and the head and pelvic movements may be integrated, both pointing to 12 then moving clockwise or anti-clockwise.

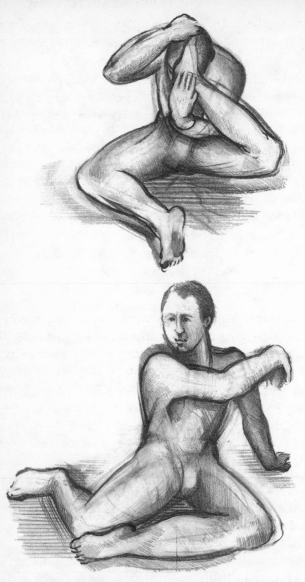

Feldenkrais brings new awareness of how you can most efficiently move different parts of the body in relation to each other.

The movements are subtle but can uncover many areas previously ignored or which feel disconnected from the rest of the body.

People tend to restrict movement where pain has been experienced, and so sensitivity gradually declines. After two or three lessons, or a weekend course, one would expect to feel a general ease of movement. Very often relief of pain leads to re-exploration of an area previously devoid of sensation. The emphasis, however, is always on simple concentrated awareness of what's happening rather than trying to accomplish anything. About 80 per cent of Feldenkrais students keep on with top-up sessions, Christopher Connolly estimates.

Who benefits?

The Feldenkrais Method is used by many people with a variety of physical problems, affecting, for example, the neck, shoulders and hips. They may simply have pain or could be recovering from injuries. Stroke victims, the physically handicapped, dancers, musicians and sports people also find the method very helpful.

Personal view

● *Georgina, 58, musician.* I've had individual lessons and gone to some weekend courses over the last five or six years. It's been rather spasmodic; I just go if I feel I need it. I haven't been one-track about it. I also use osteopathy and acupuncture; they all help each other.

As a musician I suffer some tension in my neck and shoulders. I find the whole attitude to where tensions build up very interesting. Now I can intercept problems in the early stages and sense before I would have done where a tension is coming on. Then I can side-step it. And also I can help myself if I do get hurt in any way, such as if I have lifted something in the wrong way.

The Feldenkrais way of putting more awareness in the pelvis is very useful. I'm much more aware of placing my pelvis in a flexible position when I'm driving long distance, for example. It's helpful to concentrate on that area, as it links up with so much more in your body.

Feldenkrais was also very concerned with the fact that human beings take a long time to mature, and that damage is done in early life by reacting in various ways. I can see much more clearly now the link between the emotions and the physical body.

I continue to go because I'm trying to become self-sufficient, to utilize the knowledge of myself in order to avoid becoming ill. Feldenkrais is very good for teaching you to become more aware of your own body so you are able to diagnose certain pains which you may be getting.

It's not exactly exercise, and there's no straining or pushing. They give you suggestions rather than instructions, and it's surprising the different ways people in a class will interpret those suggestions. Really you are under your own supervision, working on yourself by yourself, even in a big class. What I like is that there is no feeling of competition, and it's such a gentle way of discovering your own nervous system and how that governs the physical movement. Sometimes you get stuck and can't break the mould of previous patterns, and that's when you need some help, but then generally you find it's something quite simple that has to be changed.

I feel much more aware now of where problems arise, and I have used the knowledge I've gained to help music students, too.

Where to go

Feldenkrais Information
Centre
188 Old Street
London EC1V 9BP
Tel: 01-251-4076

Christopher Connolly
18 Kemplay Road
London NW3
Tel: 01-435-8145

MASSAGE

What is it?

Massage is one of the oldest forms of natural healing. It is thought to have been in constant use for about 5,000 years and was probably first formulated into a therapeutic system in China. It is a known part of the traditional healing systems of India and was used extensively in the ancient Greek and Roman civilizations – indeed, it is mentioned in Hippocrates' writings of around 400 BC.

Massage involves hand-on-body contact and the use of specific movements, which vary according to both the system used and the aim. The applications of massage are vast. It can be used to stimulate the body and prepare it for action, and therapeutically to help heal injury and speed up recovery to full mobility. For most people massage is probably used to relax tense muscles and invigorate the exhausted body.

Massage works on many levels. Possibly most importantly, it is a way of direct touch, with all the caring and communication that brings. As sports therapist Frank Westell says, 'Massage brings about the personal communication between one human being and another, through contact, which is becoming very rare in a touch-deficient world.'

The importance of touch in healing has been recognized formally in hospitals in the United States, where Professor Dolores Kreiger of New York University has introduced courses in 'therapeutic touch' to the nursing school curriculum. An extremely gentle, caring method, it is more a way of holding than conventional massage movements. As with all massage, she states, 'To be truly therapeutic, this act must be deeply motivated in the best interests of the person who is being touched. Although the act seems quite simple, it is in fact quite complex and the toucher must be able to understand the underlying dynamics of these complexities.'

Used in this way touching is a profound way of giving love. Its dramatic healing effects have been documented through scientific research. Therapeutic touch has been proved to cause beneficial chemical changes in a patient's blood and to alter brain waves (measured by electro-encephalogram) towards a more relaxed state of mind. Subjective reports show it to reduce pain significantly, resulting in reduced use of pain-killers in cases of arthritis and bone fracture. On a physiological level, this kind of massage, like others, may help stimulate the release of endorphins, the body's natural pain-killing and relaxant hormones, from the brain.

Physically, massage is a direct contact with the inter-related web of skin, muscles, ligaments, tendons and bones that make up 60 per cent of the human body. The effects on superficial veins of deep stroking in the direction of the blood flow are one of the most easily observed results of massage. Normal pressure on the veins is reduced and arterial circulation increased.

Lymph is another fluid that can be influenced by massage. A viscous substance that moves slowly through the lymphatic system, carrying with it much of the body's toxic waste for elimination, it depends on forces such as muscle contraction for its mobility. Massage increases the lymphatic flow, especially where it has been impaired by illness or immobility. Special slow, rhythmical massage strokes are used for this purpose.

Massage is also used to stretch muscles that have become shortened. It is this benefit that is most immediately felt, and that we often attempt to achieve by ourselves when rubbing at stiff shoulders or neck. The bunching effect of stiffened muscle can easily be felt just under the skin. The relaxation of muscle mass as a result of massage is what encourages the feeling of release and peace.

Some of the important benefits of massage are produced by working on 'trigger' or 'reflex' points. These are areas of pain and tenderness in muscle tissue, which sometimes come to light only as a masseur begins to probe. Dr Janet Travell, who has conducted major research into trigger points, discovered particular conditions to be associated with them: a sensitive trigger point in the neck, for instance, would cause teeth to over-react to heat and cold; sore points in the temporalis muscles at the sides of the head could make the eyes water. Other researchers discovered similar effects: trigger points causing muscular spasms in the neck leading to short-sightedness, reflex points in the spine relating to asthma, sinusitis and duodenal ulcers. These and other such findings provide a clear link to the principles of acupuncture, in which key points on the body are believed to govern the functions of the whole organism.

Masseur Gordon Inkeles relates trigger points to nerve activity. In his book *The New Massage* he says, 'The entire body is controlled by the brain via the nerves. Virtually all the beneficial effects of massage are directly related to changes in the nervous system.'

Massage and masseurs

Massage as we know it today is often referred to as 'Swedish' massage. The reason dates back to the 1800s, when massage as a healing therapy was revived and popularized by Swedish fencing master and gymnastics coach Per Henrik Ling. Having cured himself of rheumatism using massage, he evolved a system incorporating it with remedial exercise. The only massage extant in Europe at the time was the French system of 'mechanotherapy', the work of a doctor, Ambroise Pare, the old methods having been long forgotten.

Ling won acceptance by basing his work on the then new science of physiology. His institute in Stockholm, backed by the Swedish government, drew students from all over the world, who then established schools of 'Swedish' massage in their own countries. Orthopaedic specialist Dr James Cyriax, of St Thomas's Hospital and the King Edward Memorial Hospital in London, was particularly important to the development of massage in Britain. He advised deep friction work, coupled with 'therapeutic movements' similar to those taught by Ling, to be used on patients for between 15 and 45 minutes daily.

There are several reputable schools of massage in Britain, all of which maintain or are associated with registers of qualified masseurs and masseuses. However, there is no nationally recognized massage qualification, although the International Therapy Examination Council examines students and awards diplomas testifying to a basic knowledge of massage, anatomy and physiology. The only state-registered therapists with a tradition of using massage are physiotherapists, who have become increasingly machine, rather than hand, orientated. Osteopaths and chiropractors use massage as part of their work, but are unlikely to offer full body massage.

The main quality necessary in a massage therapist is sensitive hands. Masseurs can be trained in technique, but without the ability to communicate by touch, they will not be effective. People use that aspect of touch all the time in varying degrees – rubbing an injury, stroking a pet, holding a child. It is the development and directing of it at will that makes a successful therapist.

Stamina is probably the second requirement. Massage is hard work and a good supply of energy is needed so that the massage 'flows' without becoming heavy-handed or forceful.

What to expect

The main techniques used in massage are: *effleurage* (gliding strokes), *pétrissage* (kneading movements), *tapotement* (quick striking movements), *friction* (a kind of compression) and *vibration* (shaking action). Bare flesh makes the masseur's job much easier and results in a better, more effective massage. It helps, therefore, if clients are not bashful and remove most, or, preferably, all of their clothes. Some masseurs provide a loose fitting gown to wear, opening down the back, or, more usually, cover the client with towels and/or blankets to keep him warm and maintain modesty. A good masseur will minimize exposure, uncovering only the part of the body he is working on.

A typical massage starts with the client lying face down and the masseur making long, slow, gentle, sweeping strokes up the back from the base of the spine to the tops of the shoulders. He will gradually increase pressure, all the time noting the information his hands are receiving about texture, lumps, bumps or areas of bunched muscle. These will receive more direct treatment later.

Usually stroking movements are followed by kneading or rolling the flesh along both sides of the spine. Then the masseur may return to the more general sweeping strokes, followed by friction – more intense, small, circular movements – along the spine. Gradually the treatment moves from the general to the particular, until the masseur works on areas singled out for special attention.

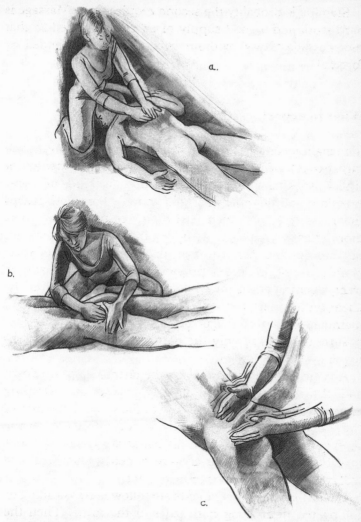

Effleurage (a), *pétrissage* (b) and *tapotement* (c) – **three basic massage movements.**

Although clients may come with a specific problem, the masseur will often seem to ignore it. Generally, physical therapists like to feel for themselves what is wrong. It could be that a pain is being triggered by a reflex point somewhere completely different (see p. 100). Often pains disappear during treatment without the painful area ever being worked on directly.

The masseur then treats the rest of the body in the same way. Some masseurs like to include the neck and shoulders when they massage the back; others may tackle this infamous problem area later when the client is fully relaxed, or at the end when he is sitting up. The common sequence is: back, shoulders, neck; the client turns over and the masseur treats the left leg from toe to knee with special reference to the calf; left thigh; then the right lower leg; the right thigh; the arms. Some therapists massage the abdomen as well. Most will finish as they started, with final attention to the back.

The total massage may take from thirty minutes to an hour or longer. Ideally, the client is left to relax for a few minutes rather than being bundled into his clothes and out of the door. Common sensations are warmth, tingling and heavy limbs, combined with slight light-headedness. Some people find massage so relaxing they are disorientated afterwards; in this case it is best to sit down until one feels better and, perhaps, be collected.

People commonly drift into sleep during massage. There need be no embarrassment about this; therapists are used to it and, indeed, it shows the therapy is successfully bringing about relaxation. Particularly, those most tense and stressed find massage has this effect, but with regular sessions relaxation becomes familiar and creeps into daily life instead of taking sudden 'shock' effect.

Massage is rarely painful, though therapists vary tremendously in their approach and some may work more deeply and harder than others. Finding the right one for you is very personal. Sometimes problem areas (and most people have trouble with tense shoulders) may give some pain when the masseur's hands get to grips with them, but it is a 'good' pain, which investigates and ultimately dissolves the dull ache of permanent tension.

Who benefits?

It seems obvious that massage can have health enhancing effects for everyone, as it soothes the entire nervous system. A 1983 report of a trial on psychiatric patients at a hospital in West Lothian, for example, showed that 30–45 minute sessions of massage were more effective than large doses of drugs in helping people cope with chronic tension and anxiety and associated muscular tension and pain. In this case the massage was so effective in symptom reduction that three out of five patients were able to cease taking drugs.

Most top sports competitors consider massage vital to performance because it stimulates the metabolism and the reabsorption and elimination of lactic acid. This waste product is formed in the muscles during aerobic exercise in proportion to the intensity and duration of the activity. In large amounts it saturates the muscles, causing that extreme tenderness or pain familiar to anyone who exercises hard. Research has shown that a mere five minutes of massage substituted for five minutes of rest causes muscle recovery to soar between 50 and 75 per cent.

Massage also plays an invaluable part in treating sports and other injuries. Research on 700 sprains and joint problems, for example, showed that sprains treated by massage recovered in one-third of the time of those treated by conventional immobilization with bandaging and strapping.

Massage has a cosmetic role too. It helps eliminate dead cells from the skin surface, thus giving the body a younger and smoother appearance. Used on the scalp, it can hold baldness at bay because of the increase in nutrient-feeding circulation.

Specialized forms of massage

Aromatherapy

Aromatherapy uses basic massage techniques to apply combinations of oils, the essences extracted from roots, flowers, leaves, bark or resin of various plants. It is akin to herbal medicine in treating disease, or imbalances in the system that could lead to disease, with appropriate plant remedies. Evidence shows the oils are absorbed directly through the skin, where they act on internal organs, and can treat almost any disorder. Clinical aromatherapy (practised mostly in France) is a medical treatment in which the oils are taken internally, but, as in the external application, massage renders the body more relaxed and receptive, and intensifies the oils' effectiveness.

Apart from its medical benefits, aromatherapy is a luxurious treatment in its own right, a wonderful way of relaxing while inhaling the aroma of the natural oils.

Intuitive massage

Many therapists prefer to call their massage intuitive, rather than stating an adherence to any particular school or technique. To some extent all massage is intuitive; it comes out of the therapist's sense of what is needed at the time, with that particular client's body. The best massage supersedes technique and creates a harmony of its own. It is important, though, that the therapist has a structure on which to base intuition, otherwise he might miss signs of real physical disorder.

Neuro-muscular technique (NMT)

This is a precise form of massage that can be used to diagnose, not just to treat. It works on the fascia, an elastic connective tissue rich in nerve endings, which sheathes and supports muscles (see pp. 147–9). Directly or indirectly, most massage works on this connective tissue, but only NMT diagnoses and treats directly through fascia.

First systematized by chiropractor and osteopath Stanley Lief and his cousin Boris Chaitow in the 1940s, NMT has been developed by naturopath and osteopath Leon Chaitow. His aim has been to simplify the many different trigger, or reflex, points that cover the body and to work on connective tissue in these areas, believing that sensitive hands will be able to detect a potential disease process and, by early treatment, prevent chronic problems. 'In skilled hands', says Leon Chaitow, 'NMT can remove pain, improve function, obviate manipulation or prepare for it, enhance the body's economy and greatly aid in the restoration of health.'

Reflexology

Reflexology is a foot massage based on the theory that specific points on the feet, and to some extent the hands, correspond to, and reflect the condition of, all the body's structures. Thus each foot presents a detailed 'map' of the body.

The thumb and index finger are the reflexologist's main tools. Moving with a caterpillar-like action across each 'reflex' he can help relax and heal the connected part. While the benefits can be therapeutic for the whole system, what most people experience predominantly is a deep sense of peace and relaxation.

Shiatsu

In this therapy pressure is applied to the pathways, or

meridians, in the body along which the life force flows. Each one is associated with a specific body organ or function. The therapist uses his own instruments of massage some-what creatively; he may apply pressure with the thumb or the palm, the knee or the elbow, even the soles of the feet (it is not unknown for a client to be walked on). The aim is to stimulate or relax energy channels according to need, very much as acupuncture does but without the needles. The technique is ancient and very well tried and tested over thousands of years. Some pain may be experienced, but only for a few seconds, and the result is a sense of balance and well-being.

Like reflexology, shiatsu is a highly specialized treatment with its own training and professional associations.

Personal view

● *Brendan, 36, colour technician.* The first time I had a
   real massage was after I broke my knee and needed
   some treatment to help me ride my bike again. I felt
   the benefit straight away; it allowed the joint to repair
   itself. Since then I've had massage sporadically a
   number of times, for different reasons. I don't think
   you can just talk about 'massage' – it depends on what
   you have it for. It can be actual treatment for ailments,
   to restore circulation, to get muscles working again, for
   recovery after sport, as part of a training programme
   and also for stress and tension.

   I can honestly say it's never been wasted on me.
   Massage is the only form of therapy that always works
   in some way, specially if you are subject to stress and
   tension, as I am. It's incredibly important to be
   massaged, and very few people are. Even if people are
   massaged regularly without anything being wrong, it

probably prevents them becoming ill and certainly avoids tensions.

The kind of massage that works on me wouldn't necessarily be right for someone else. Gentle massage is nice, but because I have problems with muscle tension I need a deep and vigorous massage. I find it very hard to stretch my muscles but after a massage everything feels much looser.

What I think is really important is that massage is a direct aid to mental relaxation and hence makes it much easier to access your own self-healing ability – as well as the immediate physical benefits. It also helps me sleep.

Where to go

London and Counties
Society of Physiologists
100 Waterloo Road
Blackpool, Lancashire
FY4 1AW
Tel: 0253-403548

Fellowship of Sports
Masseurs and Therapists
BM Soigneur
London WC1N 3XX

International Federation of
Aromatherapists
41 Eastmeaen Road
Dulwich, London SE21 8HA

Association of Tisserand
Aromatherapists
3 Shirley Street
Hove, East Sussex BN3 3WJ
Tel: 0273-772479

Association of Reflexologists
37 Standale Grove
Ruislip, Middlesex HA4 7UA
Tel: 0895-635621

British Reflexology
Association
1A Laund Nook
Belper, Derby DE5 1JY
Tel: 077-382 2033

Shiatsu Society
19 Langside Park
Kilbarchan, Renfrewshire
PA10 2EP
Tel: 05057-4657

PILATES

What is it?

Pilates is a non-aerobic method of exercising by lengthening and stretching all the major muscle groups in a balanced way, using a system of apparatus. What distinguishes it from being 'just' another form of exercise is that it is entirely customized: an individual programme is worked out for each person at a Pilates exercise studio. The client is taught the correct way to do the exercises, which may be changed by the teacher as the body alters shape and has new needs.

Most important is the system's emphasis on posture correction and balance. It strengthens muscles because it is well-functioning muscle groups that support the right kind of movement – standing up straight without stooping, walking with ease, carrying shopping with the least amount of fatigue. The right use of these muscles in everyday life will improve total function of the body, with the improvement in mental areas, such as alertness and clarity, that comes from feeling good physically.

The balancing is achieved almost automatically. The system is designed so that instead of favouring and over-developing stronger muscles, the student works on and strengthens weaker ones, and the action of each muscle group gradually equalizes. Alan Herdman, who teaches the technique in London, explains, 'When you observe many people you see that they stand almost in an "S" bend: the stomach muscles have fallen out so the lower back is much more curved than it should be. That means the upper torso is also curved and they get a lot of tension in the neck and shoulders. Just by aiming at strengthening the centre, the abdominal area, they can be supported in the lower back, which helps them to stand up straight. Then, once they've got this strength in the centre, they can hold the whole upper torso in the correct position.'

The third component in Pilates is the incorporation of breathing with the phases of an exercise. Clients are taught to breathe rhythmically, harmoniously and easily, using the lungs to their full depth. Although hard to co-ordinate at first, it gets to be second nature as the exercises themselves become habitual.

Pilates work is essentially very safe, possibly more so than other forms of exercise just because it is supervised throughout. Doctors and osteopaths have given it their blessing and Pilates teachers work closely with physiotherapists, who like the fact that it is applied carefully and individually. On many occasions the physiotherapist may determine precisely where work needs to be done after injury and the Pilates class will adapt to that particular requirement. The client concentrates on this specific area of the body, which may be supported at first while she works round it, ensuring that the whole area does not become weakened and gradually building up until the injured part is ready to start working again.

Origins of Pilates

Joseph Pilates was born in Germany in 1880 and, like many other pioneers in the physical therapies, his own frailty as a child made him determined to become strong and healthy. By the time he was a teenager he had succeeded. By working at body-building techniques he developed his muscles so well that he became a model for anatomical drawings. When he came to England just before the First World War Pilates worked as a boxer, circus performer and self-defence teacher. During the war he was interned on the Isle of Man, where in the enforced leisure, he began devising his technique.

The idea had been with him for some time. He felt that the body-building methods he had adopted should not be used just for physical education, but incorporated into a system of posture correction and thus help the development of the whole person rather than an isolated aspect.

After the war Pilates returned to Germany. There he met and worked closely with Rudolph Laban (see p. 176) for a while. In the 1920s Pilates left for New York, en route meeting and marrying Clara, whose own ideas about exercise fused with and encouraged his. In New York they immediately set up their first exercise studio and the system took off.

Elsewhere the Pilates method stayed virtually unknown. It was brought to Britian in 1970 by Alan Herdman, an ex-primary school teacher turned dancer, who had trained in New York with one of Pilates' disciples. Although he sticks to the basic Pilates method, Herdman is master enough to use his own interpretations without losing the method's original focus. It is most important, he feels, to stay faithful to Pilates' ideas of posture correction and realignment: 'When dealing with a technique that is to correct people's problems you can't bend the person to suit the technique, you must bend the technique to suit the person you're working with. Pilates said it was all about physical and mental conditioning. So you can't just go through the motions. People must work individually, for their needs, and think very carefully what they're doing.'

With Pilates' principles in mind, the teacher can constantly re-evaluate so that the method is flexible enough to meet the needs of everyone who uses it. New trainees are appearing and the system is gaining ground for its solidity and gimmick-free effectiveness.

What to expect

By far the most popular, and recommended, way to do Pilates work is to attend a Pilates studio. Studio sessions take from an hour to an hour and a quarter, and two or three attendances a week are recommended. Like other forms of exercise, the more you do it, the more you get out of it.

At first glance the studios look like an elegant gym. There are ropes and pulleys, slant boards and tables that slide back and forth on a smooth spring system. In fact, a second look will confirm that all the equipment is unlike anything seen in a conventional work-out room. It is specially made along the lines laid down by Joseph Pilates.

The atmosphere of the studio, too, contradicts the standard exercise milieu. Here is no sweating or straining. To a background of classical music, people of all ages pursue their individual routines, concentrating intensely. The sense of quiet harmony is more like a yoga class than a work-out session. Appointments are booked throughout the day to keep numbers manageable.

The first time you go to the studio you will be given an assessment session. This is where you are introduced to the equipment and watched by the Pilates teacher as you attempt the exercises. A few glances are enough to show the competent teacher where your weaknesses and your strengths are, which muscles need to work harder and where you are overcompensating. The way you turn your torso, the strength with which you stretch your legs immediately reveal the condition of your muscles and the way they've been treated.

While there is a basic Pilates sequence, your programme is customized by the degree to which exercises are added or omitted and by the proportionate timings. Special problems are taken into account and in the end your session is geared to your body alone.

The unique Pilates equipment allows you to stretch major muscles without strain.

After your sequence is established, you work through it at your own pace. Each exercise has five or ten repetitions. There is no danger of doing an exercise incorrectly, for an expert eye will quickly pick up any misdemeanours and you will be put right gently. The studio is unhurried and there are rarely more than four students under the eye of one instructor.

The exercises are deceptively simple. On one piece of equipment, for example, you will be asked to lie on your back and move the legs up and down in a ballet *plié* action, so the knees part and the bar on which your feet are pressing moves against your resistance. It is not difficult to push the bar, which is on springs. But the trick is to work at it, locating the muscles that are most involved and stretching and contracting them each time. In this particular exercise the feet change position for its three phases, working calves, ankles and inner and outer thighs.

The session leaves no part of the body unstretched, no tiny muscle untouched. After leg work, you deal with stomach and torso, gradually doing the rounds of the apparatus. One of the most appealing aspects of the method is that, although hard work, it does not leave you perspiring and exhausted. 'I've always maintained that this thing about going for the burn is awful. The muscles start burning when they're being over-used. I want this feeling of well-being to be the most important thing. When people work carefully and deeply their muscles work correctly without exhaustion,' says Alan Herdman.

Taking care means the studio has no room for impatience. 'If you try to be too quick, you start to use the muscles incorrectly. I've seen it many times in the past, where people have been pushed in exercise routines. They are defeating the object because when they work too hard, they grip too much and tense the muscles. It shouldn't work like that.'

Concentration is all important and cannot be stressed enough. The small pupil-teacher ratio goes a long way to ensure that classes do not become mechanical. 'If it doesn't work individually with people you've lost what it's about,' Alan Herdman says. He is the first to admit the possibility of boredom, particularly since repetition is an integral part of the Pilates exercises and essential for their success. 'Every time someone came, I could show them different, entertaining exercises to do, but we wouldn't be getting anywhere. It would just be a case of doing flashy exercises, pitting my knowledge of the technique against their ability to do it. That wouldn't give you the basis for building up strength and getting the correct posture, which is what I want.'

How do you overcome the tedium of repeating the same exercises three times a week? 'You've just got to carry people through that plateau, the difficult times when you coast along. With help, you can then get on to the next level.'

The next level is a result of constant re-evaluation. 'You keep looking at why you're doing an exercise with someone and seeing if it would be better to change, to drop it altogether, to add something. We're always doing that, suddenly thinking an exercise isn't valid any more to suit the individual.'

Results depend very much on the person. Some react more quickly than others. By ten classes most people see a difference, even if it is just that they are standing marginally straighter than they have done for years. While the sense of dedication and inner attention echoes a yoga class, the aims are comparable to the Alexander Technique. Pilates has more to do with activity, but ultimately the same loss of tension and overall non-interference in body use is achieved.

Perhaps the most noticeable physical change is that bodies actually alter shape. People do not necessarily lose weight – in fact, some complain they are heavier on the scales. Alan Herdman, though, asks them two leading questions: can they get into their clothes? and what does the mirror say? The usual answer is that their clothes are loose and the mirror friendly. The conclusion is that by tightening and firming muscle groups, you become sturdier and firm, with a look that can best be described as sleek. Muscle is heavier than fat, accounting for the change in the scales, so 'Go by the mirror instead,' advises Alan Herdman.

At that stage, alas, you cannot sit back and admire the new body. Continued classes are essential if you want to maintain the look and sensations. For most people they become part of life, a routine that, as with any other physical fitness method, pays appreciable dividends.

For people who cannot get to a studio often, home sessions are possible. They are not, however, for the uninitiated. Rather, they are adjuncts to studio sessions, where your teacher constructs a routine that you follow faithfully.

Naturally, at home you are unsupported by equipment, but the movements can be replicated. Alan Herdman has drawn up a complete system using nothing more complicated than the floor, a chair and a towel. The home routines are meant to last only about ten minutes. Alan Herdman recognizes and accepts people's psychology: 'If it was any longer, no one would do it.'

Who benefits?

A lot of dancers and other performers who need their bodies to be in tip-top condition go to Pilates classes. Many of them may have injuries from bad body use. Ballet dancers are the worst culprits, because of imposed positions that have been incorrect for them. Alan Herdman works closely with dance remedial clinics, but admits it is often easier to work on non-dancers who have a 'clean plate' and no need to break down old, bad training habits. The main problems among the general public are damaged knees and lower backs. Skiing injuries are common. Tension in the upper back is also frequently presented, but is often secondary and referred because of bad posture. Everyone, of any age and with whatever tough, chronic problem, is welcome and can improve with hard work. 'The important thing is that for most people who suffer from the universal backache, there is normally nothing wrong with their physique. It's just the way they sit and stand and move and the tension that goes into the lower back because of that bad posture. The problem becomes chronic because of various factors, but the injured area can be supported and strengthened while it heals through this method,' promises Alan Herdman.

Personal views

● *Margaret, 49, store buyer*. I started exercising five years ago. I did one year of aerobics, then got bored with it and looked around for something else. When I first saw the Pilates method it seemed rather difficult, but I thought I'd give it a try. I found it hard to remember the sequences at first, but the instruction was good and what really helped was that it was all individual. They were very encouraging. Now I've got the feeling for it, I really enjoy doing it. I go three times a week for about an hour and a quarter.

I can go round on my own now, but someone always has an eye on you. I still have to try to make sure I'm doing the exercises properly. It's also very important to breathe correctly in conjunction with the exercises, and they teach you how to do that.

My body has more definition and the muscles supporting my bust, in particular, have improved and so has the shape of my waist and legs. I've also got more stamina. I walk and hold myself better and feel better generally about myself. It does seem to exercise everything. If I don't go to one of my regular sessions, my body misses it.

I'm impressed at how many professional dancers come here, and yet it's also good for middle-aged ladies like me. I really think it's fabulous.

● *Rosamund, 60, designer*. I originally started when I was looking for something suitable for my husband, who has Parkinson's disease. They've worked out a programme for him that seems to help. I got hooked and come twice a week. They set a programme according to what suits you. I have a back problem so I have to be a bit careful, but they know that and don't encourage you to do anything that will be harmful.

Now I can still play tennis and ski. In fact, I don't have to do ski warm-ups, as I already do the Pilates knee and ankle exercises. This is better than anything else I've done, as it makes you control your own muscles. If you go too fast you're told to slow down and really use your muscles, so you do have to think and concentrate on what you're doing.

I've tightened up a lot of muscles, in particular my thigh muscles, which were very slack before. It's made me feel a lot fitter and I'm also more conscious of my breathing, walking and how I'm standing.

I also like it because it's not pretentious or slick. They do introduce humour in the class but it's all quite serious generally; you come here to train and do your work, then off you go, feeling fitter.

Where to go

Alan Herdman Studios
17 Homer Row
London W1
Tel: 01-723-9953

POLARITY

THERAPY

What is it?

Polarity is a four-part system that synthesizes Eastern and Western healing concepts. The first clue to understanding it is to look at the human body rather like a battery. Polarity therapists see the body as a continual circulation of energy. The head is a positive pole; the feet, negative. The right hand is positive; the left, negative. This energy flows into all areas of our being and keeps us vital and able, or ebbs and renders us sick and weak.

The idea of interrelating energy movements within the body is predominantly Eastern. The therapy's originator, American Randolph Stone, travelled and researched Oriental healing methods for many years. Ultimately, he discovered that there is only one cause of acute disease: the blocking of energy, the basic life force. All the major systems he looked at have this as a common theme, and all have their own word for this energy: in India it is called *prana*; in China, *chi*; in Japan *ki*. Although invisible and immeasurable by any scientific method, it forms the essential connection between breath, mind and consciousness, and thus influences the whole body. Illness occurs when the flow of this energy becomes disturbed, then ceases altogether in one area or another.

Stone was influenced by the Chinese concept of yin and yang, or opposites that are manifested everywhere, as in light and dark, hot and cold, and so on. These 'polarities' were the concepts governing the naming of his therapy which, like the Chinese practice of acupuncture, aims to create a free flow of energy along the meridians, or pathways, in the body. Stone, however, favoured the Indian systems that use the hands to influence the energy of the body. He believed that only human contact could engender the healing process, without the involvement of anything mechanical or external. About the use of acupuncture needles he said 'There is nothing that the needles can do that the hands can't do better with a battery of consciousness behind them.'

The idea of moving people's energy is universal and Dr Stone maintained that it is basically very simple. 'You have to go under the symptom to get at the cause of things. You have to feel the other person inside of you. You have to feel their health and their sickness inside of you, and then you understand what to do and you just do it,' he said. Since all human beings have these currents of energy flowing through them, patient and therapist act in conjunction. Hence Dr Stone's insistence that the hands can do it all. If the therapist places his left hand on the patient's head (positive), and puts the other hand towards the feet or the lower pelvis (negative), a balanced effect will be created between the different areas.

Making 'good connections', that is, creating a balanced or natural energy flow, is central to the healing process. Obviously, it is a particularly subtle idea, but it is no flight of fancy. 'Every time you touch somebody, you're going to modify or change the process of energy flow in their body', explains polarity therapist Philip Young. We can feel it whoever we are with, if we allow ourselves to develop that kind of sensitivity. With some people we feel, literally, warm. Others may have a chilling effect. Each one of us 'gives out' something in an energetic, or non-verbal, way whether we feel drained or tired, vital and sparkling, or anything in between. It is certain that all of us affect each other in a variety of unspoken, subtle but none the less powerful ways.

The four techniques and the five elements

Polarity therapy influences the life energy of the body through four techniques. First is bodywork, the hands-on healing manipulation of the energy within the body. Second is diet and nutrition, since one of the major sources of life energy in the body comes through food. Third is a simple system of movement, called polarity yoga. Central to these exercises is the squatting position, which imitates the position of the foetus in the womb. It is, therefore, the position of our most important growth period and, Dr Stone believed, when re-adopted, aligns the body with the universal life energy. The exercises, which incorporate a gentle, rhythmic movement and are designed to shift energy in the body, are as calming as sitting in a rocking chair.

A person's state of mind also affects the life force. If he dwells on negativity and fear, the flow of energy is impeded in the body, making him more vulnerable to disease. Therefore, the fourth technique is counselling people to correct unhelpful states of mind, encouraging them to develop a more positive attitude so they do not damage their health.

Polarity therapists look at the five qualities, or elements, at play within the life energy – ether, air, fire, water and earth – which are relevant to all the techniques. For instance, in terms of diet, vegetables growing beneath the surface of the ground are considered to be earth foods and relate to the earth energy in the body. They tend to be warming and stabilizing. Water foods, such as salad vegetables and melons, grow above the surface. Grains contain a preponderance of fire energy, since they need sun to make them ripe. Fruits and nuts, which grow high off the ground, are said to have a lot of air energy.

On an emotional level, the fire element manifesting in its

negative sense relates to anger. Its opposite is energy, dynamism, joy and laughter. Earth energy also moves in two directions: towards stability and security, or towards instability and weakness.

The therapist uses these elements to help effect a balanced reaction. He works with the natural tendency of the energy flow and uses food to complement the main type of energy the person is 'running' on. A highly emotional person would be 'prescribed' watery food, for example, while a nervous, active individual will benefit from a high proportion of air element food.

The system may sound complicated, but it provides a deep and highly effective picture of the interrelationships within one human being. The guiding principle in looking at the five elements in the four areas of polarity therapy is to encourage, in Dr Stone's words, the 'free, full flow of energy'.

Randolph Stone and polarity therapy

Dr Randolph Stone formulated polarity therapy out of a lifetime of original work. He studied at the quaintly-named Eclectic Centre for Drugless Healing in Chicago, Illinois, during the early 1900s. There he learned the two major natural healing systems of the time: physical manipulation, which included osteopathy, chiropractic and a related form of spinal work called napropathy; and naturopathy, which included dietary reform, hydrotherapy, colonic irrigation and other cleansing methods. The result of this training was called an 'other licence', which allowed him to function in every way as an ordinary doctor even though his training had been totally different.

Then Stone began to feel dissatisfied. He asked (as do many therapists to this day) why it was that patients continued to come back even when successfully treated. Joints could be put right and spines go back into place but, even when the patient had been counselled about the correct ways of movement and had followed instructions to the letter, often exactly the same thing would go wrong again for no apparent reason. Stone was determined to find a way of keeping patients well.

During the late 1930s and early 1940s he travelled throughout Europe, then on to India and China. He looked at every indigenous healing system he could find: acupuncture, reflexology (see p. 107), Ayurvedic medicine, native Egyptian and ancient Hebrew methods. To these schools of thought he married his own training in physical manipulation, diet and detoxification. Highly eclectic, Dr Stone's unique and comprehensive system of medicine brings the healing practices of the East to the common-sense skills of the West. He devoted the rest of his life to spreading the word about his discoveries, most particularly in a five-volume series of books written in the 1950s.

Stone was a man of great spiritual discipline and tremendous presence, performing meditation practices that enabled him to get in touch at will with the energy flow in his own body. The ability to heal, he felt, came from the work the therapist did on himself. 'It wasn't his words that held the power', remembers a past student, Richard Heckler. 'It was the way he said them and the light and life that came from his bodily presence. When he actually worked with people, his spirit simply connected with the spirit of his client. Despite his vast knowledge and learning, it was really how Dr Stone brought himself to each situation that inspired life and understanding.'

What to expect

Every polarity therapist has an individual style, so do not expect to receive a standard treatment. In particular, the two training establishments in Britain (see p. 131) have slightly divergent views on what should be included in a treatment and their therapists will reflect those ideas. For example, bodywork is the heart of the therapy, but while one therapist may have that and exercises as his speciality, another might lay more emphasis on counselling or diet.

The polarity therapist is trained in a very special way. While a good grounding in anatomy is required so that he can recognize what is going on where, the therapist must be skilled enough to pick up very subtle signals through his hands. Most of us have that skill to some extent, but largely undeveloped. Developing it is simply a matter of practice in picking up a subtle degree of sensation by using what Philip Young calls 'your quality of consciousness, your degree of attention'. For example, whereas the kind of messages an unskilled person might get on touching another are of muscle tension, hard or soft skin, clamminess or warmth, the polarity therapist learns to be particularly sensitive to any tingling, throbbing or jumping, no matter how small, or to minute changes in temperature. He uses these sensations to tell him about what is happening to the all-important energy flow within the human battery, whether it is connecting and circulating as it should or is disrupted in its circuit. The messages your body gives will tell the therapist all he needs to know about the kind of blockages in the flow, whether they are chronic or temporary, and what he needs to do about them.

Every polarity therapy session incorporates a certain amount of bodywork and then the patient is given specific exercises to do at home. Dietary change, exercise and adopting a more positive attitude are all ways in which patients can feel more involved in their own cure.

The essence of a session is gentleness, as any force creates tension and blocks the life energy. The patient does very little other than lie down and make himself comfortable. The therapist's hands will be felt softly pressing or holding. Mostly, patients feel little other than the most pleasant, light touch (in fact, many people go to sleep), but the therapist is 'tuning in' to a variety of signals and working to create new currents of energy. The way he influences the energy flow involves transferring messages from his own consciousness and waiting patiently for the patient's body to respond. The released energy flow is sometimes experienced by the patient as a sudden relaxation of the tissue, a change in temperature or tingling. Occasionally, though, the effects may be more dramatic. When someone is particularly sensitive to the therapy, he could experience dizziness or even nausea. These are signs of energy shifts and, therefore, that the therapy is working.

A session of bodywork may end with structural balancing. This comes straight out of Dr Stone's chiropractic background. It is a method of balancing a person in relation to gravity, so that he is standing straight and without stressing the joints. Although a relatively physical manipulation, it is not to do with leverage in a conventional chiropractic sense. Because energy is being manipulated, finger pressure alone is enough to realign the spinal vertebrae.

'Dr Stone's idea was that energy is the blueprint and the physical body reflects the pattern of energy,' explains Philip Young. 'So if you rebalance the energy, then the physical structure will automatically follow, not the other way round. While you have to understand the relationship between the pelvis and the shoulders, and the head and the sacrum, balancing the energy in the spine will allow it to

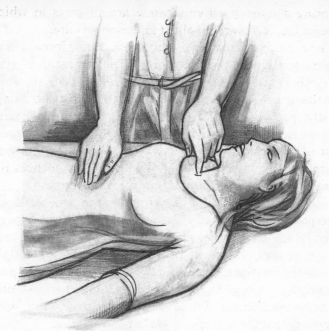

The Polarity Therapist treating thyroid gland and pancreas.

realign itself and go back into place on its own. Then the joint will settle back into position better, and will work in relation to other joints in a balanced fashion.'

After an average 45-minute session (although the initial treatment may take an hour to an hour and a half), the patient will often feel refreshed but not cured. The healing effect may come during the following days or after a return visit. Rarely is a protracted period of treatment recommended, except when a patient is involved in serious emotional disturbances or is coming off drugs. Philip Young asks patients to commit themselves to three sessions, expecting to see many changes during that time. If there is no response by the fourth session, he says, it might take as many as twenty and in that case it might be better for the patient to try another kind of therapy.

Who benefits?

Virtually everybody can benefit from this therapy. Polarity therapists, in common with other practitioners, tend to see a lot of patients with bad backs, while those with digestive disorders and emotional problems run a close second. 'I think I've seen just about every problem there is,' says Philip Young. Children are particularly quick to respond to polarity therapy because their vital energy is higher and quicker. Surprisingly, the elderly are also good candidates, especially if they are of the old school who 'don't believe in doctors' and therefore have systems uncontaminated by drugs. The simple action of physical contact may also be useful for those living alone.

Personal views

● *Bettie, 35, housewife.* I came to polarity therapy when I was heavily pregnant two years ago with my fifth child and had a back problem – the baby was pulling a vertebra out of place. There was nothing I could do about the cause except wait for the baby to be born. It was very distressing.

I was so impressed after the first session I couldn't get back quickly enough. Then after the baby was born, I was seriously ill. I had a fall and that damaged the vertebra which had been weakened previously. Polarity work was especially helpful, as I was too ill for other forms of treatment. I couldn't walk, I could hardly see, I was almost suicidal. I was in a very bad way.

It helped in all directions. It's a three-fold therapy (I wasn't well enough for the exercises), with the hands-on work, the diet and counselling. I could really feel subtle changes in each session. It was especially dramatic on the emotional side. I went from feeling totally despairing to seeing a light at the end of the tunnel. I think it can really help people with post-natal depression; for me it was like lifting an enormous burden, and that makes a difference not only to you but to everyone round you. And women will sympathize when I say that if you feel you are getting somewhere with your emotional state, then you feel better physically too.

I reached a point after six or eight sessions – going regularly once a week for two months – where I had achieved something. I was shifting the energy down my back myself, using polarity breathing exercises, and so I could straighten my own back and sleep at the end of a long hard day.

Now, although I get very tired, I can still walk and I'm relatively pain-free. That's a miracle in itself. So although I live in rather a crisis situation, polarity therapy has been a real lifeline to me.

● *Viv, 45, college counsellor.* I've had 18 years of an extremely stressful life and felt very ill when I first heard of polarity therapy. By then I had been hospitalized for two weeks and was fighting breast cancer. My health problems really started when my husband died and I hadn't allowed myself to grieve for him. Physically I knew things were really wrong – in fact, I thought I was going to die.

I'm very open-minded and I'll try anything, and I got a good feeling from the polarity therapist when I met him at a centre for complementary medicine where

I was staying. What he said about the therapy made a good deal of sense, so I thought I'd give it a whirl. Well, I told him nothing about my health problems, so you can imagine how surprised I was when the first thing he did was put a hand on my right breast, and also over my pubic area. I thought, 'what's going on?' but anyway I let him get on with it; after all he was a professional therapist.

I had three sessions on that occasion and I had such a calm, tranquil feeling after each one, which stayed for several hours. It was the first time I'd felt at peace for a long, long time. Since then I've been back for treatments every month. I find it balances whatever is out of 'synch'. I don't understand what happens, but you just have to let it be. It's a very difficult thing to explain. It makes me feel good and very tranquil but it also raises a lot of emotions. Last time I felt quite negative after a session, as I couldn't deal with all the emotions that were coming up, so it's not 100 per cent peaceful. But I feel whatever comes up, I must let it happen, because I'm usually the sort of person who's forever trying to push things down. So much of the time my life feels out of control, but gradually the therapy feels like it's de-stressing me.

I do think it's a matter of going to the right therapist, not just having the therapy. Particularly with polarity, the therapist has to give out a sense of balance, and not everyone has that. It wouldn't be fair to say that I'm entirely cured, but this therapist is certainly right for me.

Where to go

International School of
Polarity Therapy
8 West Allington
Bridport, Dorset DT6 5BG
Tel: 0308-23659

Polarity Therapy Association
Curtisknowle House
Curtisknowle
near Totnes, Devon
Tel: 054-882-425

RELAXATION

What is it?

Most people think they know how to relax. It may be by sitting down with a drink on getting home from work, or by watching television or leafing lazily through the Sunday papers. Many of us have active ways of relaxing: playing golf, gardening, going for a ramble or taking the dog for a walk.

While any of these may feel good, though, they do not always bring about complete relaxation, for deep relaxation causes actual physical changes. When practised regularly, well-tried relaxation methods produce scientifically measurable results encompassing a sense of well-being but reaching far beyond it.

We need relaxation, quite simply, to discharge stress. The problem is that stress creeps up on us in ever-increasing layers. So prevalent is it in modern life that we accept high levels as normal and attempt to carry on without really listening to what our bodies are saying. Even when we follow so-called 'relaxing' pursuits, we may never completely shift the total burden of anxiety and tension. Indeed, even sleep may not be as relaxing as we think. There is evidence that the physiological system may still be at high arousal level although we think we have 'switched off'.

Stress

To understand relaxation, it is first necessary to look at what stress is and the effects it has on us. In simple terms stress is the physical and emotional reaction to any kind of external threat. It has both positive and negative aspects. It stimulates us to face the challenges of the day. We can actually enjoy it when we experience it, in friendlier terms, as excitement or a flow of adrenalin. Many people can cope with, or even thrive on, a large degree of stress and actively seek it out.

We all are programmed to deal with stress of a particular kind. What Kenneth Pelletier, researcher into neurophysiology and psychosomatic medicine, calls a 'normal adaptive stress reaction' occurs when we meet a clear source of stress, for instance a moment of physical danger. Probably everyone can recall the quickening of the heart beat, trembling, stomach churning, muscle clenching, bowel loosening, and other familiar symptoms. This reaction is also known as the 'fight or flight' response, as all our bodily resources are geared to do one or the other in a threatening situation. When the challenge is over, these quickly abate, breathing returns to normal and we may feel a rush of exhaustion.

The trouble comes when this return to normal is somehow prevented from happening. This occurs when stress comes from a generalized, unclear and/or continuing source and when several stressors are at play simultaneously. In his book *Mind as Healer, Mind as Slayer*, Kenneth Pelletier identifies several categories of such stress triggers. First is the environment, which includes general stressors such as air and noise pollution, urban overcrowding, job pressures and deadlines, competition in work and domestic life. Second come negative events – financial difficulties, the death of close relatives, for example. Third are personal relationships, for instance conflict with someone at work, with a child, or a spouse. Research into the life events most likely to trigger personal stress has also been done by Thomas Holmes and Richard Rahe of the University of Washington. They rate death of a spouse highest, followed by divorce, marital separation and gaol sentence.

Interestingly, events generally considered 'positive' may cause stress too – holidays, promotions at work and marriage.

Kenneth Pelletier explains that reactions to stress also become stress factors in their own right. Thus we may have a number of disturbing symptoms that seem to have no direct correlation to present events, but they worry us enough to create their own stress: general anxiety, sleep disturbances, depression.

In these conditions we experience some degree of stress all the time, and it is never discharged. By the end of what is known as a 'normal' working day, our stress levels may have reached the same proportions as if we were in the midst of battle. The essential difference is that because the stress sources are so diverse (and also because there is often social pressure to withstand them stoically) we put them to one side and ignore our physiological state. We are, in effect, still switched on to 'fight or flight' irrespective of any immediate danger. And while the glass of whisky or round of golf can help dissolve the top level of reaction, deeper work is needed to shift it completely.

The stress reactions are intricately bound up with the nervous system, which may be described graphically as our electrical wiring circuit. The nervous system has two main components: voluntary and involuntary, or autonomic. The voluntary system is responsible for all movement that is under our obvious control, such as physical posture. Involuntary, or autonomic, action governs everything over which we appear to have no conscious control, like the gastro-intestinal and circulatory functions. It is the autonomic system that causes the neurophysical and biochemical changes that we feel as stress. The autonomic functions in which stress is particularly easily measurable are brain wave activity, heart rate and regularity, muscle tension, blood pressure and peripheral circulation.

Perhaps the most important factor in modern stress control research is the discovery that we can, in fact, influence the working of this involuntary system and that it is far from being as totally 'automatic' as was thought. The 'relaxation response', a term coined by another important researcher, Dr Herbert Benson of the Harvard Medical School, can be learned and influences deep within the brain.

The autonomic system itself has two parts: the sympathetic and parasympathetic nervous systems. The sympathetic constricts and tenses muscles and activates the endocrine system. In general it causes what we feel as excitation. The parasympathetic, conversely, is the primary relaxation-inducing mechanism. Different people react to stress in widely different ways. Although in most people the most common reaction is the overactivity of the sympathetic nervous system, causing tension, coolness, rigidity and general contraction, in some people it is the parasympathetic system that overreacts instead, resulting in extreme tiredness and, possibly, low blood pressure. An example of this difference can be seen in the action of the heart: rapid pulsating and stopping altogether can both be stress reactions.

Why relax?

Dr Malcolm Carruthers, researcher into stress, says that we all have different loading capacities on our nervous system circuits. Overloading the circuits causes problems in many ways. 'When the load becomes too much, we blow a fuse. Some people – like Mrs Thatcher – have a 30 amp cooker fuse. Others, more sensitive creative types, have only a 3 or 5 amp lighting fuse.' The person who 'works well under pressure' is the one with the stronger fuse. He is also more likely to be able to discharge stress fully when the pressure is off.

There is no knowing where in the body the blown fuse will appear. Some people will collapse under a weighty headache or react in the gut, with constipation or diarrhoea. Others may come out in spots or eczema attacks, have indigestion, insomnia, muscular spasm and pain. They may become irritable or depressed or subject to mood swings. These signs may be precursors to other, more serious responses.

The essential key to stress control, says Dr Carruthers, is to recognize your type of circuit and when you are about to blow a fuse, and to learn ways of balancing the activities of sympathetic and parasympathetic systems.

Studies indicate that stress and its effects touch on every aspect of our functioning. Kenneth Pelletier believes that from 50 to 80 per cent of all disorders have stress-related links. Most likely are ulcers, colitis, bronchial asthma, dermatitis, hay fever, arthritis, hypertension (high blood pressure), hyperthyroiditis, amenorrhoea (loss of menstrual periods), enuresis (bed-wetting) and migraine. Hypertension is possibly the most dangerous of all since, in extreme cases, it is implicated in heart attack, stroke and kidney disease. Pelletier considers that in the four most common diseases in the Western world – heart disorders, cancer, arthritis and respiratory malfunction – 'the increased psychosocial stress of post-industrial societies' is a major contributing factor.

Even when stress has not taken so great a toll on our health, it hinders us in many ways. Quite simply, when stressed we tend to function less efficiently. Athletes and sports people all over the world recognize the role of relaxation and apply it in physical events instead of pushing the body with ever more effort and tension.

Relaxation teacher James Hewitt takes the need for relaxation even further. In his book *Relaxation East and West*, he terms relaxation 'poised living'. He says, 'It is connected

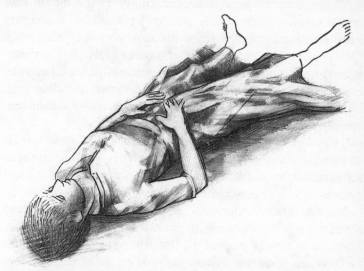

The perfectly relaxed body functions better in all situations.

with the profoundest experiences known to human consciousness, however you choose to interpret them. Relaxation followed right through offers a way – even in the Eastern sense of a mystical "path" – to expansion of consciousness, to greater freedom from conditioning, to spiritual unfoldment and experiential wisdom. It is a lifestyle for the development of full humanness (self-actualization) and for letting go and opening up to the mindfulness of being.'

Ways of relaxing

There is a long tradition of stress-reducing techniques. The oldest are seen in the yoga and meditation practices of the East, showing recognition even 5,000 years ago of our capacity for distraction and anxiety, and our need for relaxation. These methods of relaxing are still much favoured today and have made a dramatic impression on the West in recent years.

In addition, in response to the needs of modern civilization and what Malcolm Carruthers calls the 'pooled, over-stimulating stress' we must withstand, several new techniques have arisen. These new methods are based on learning specific muscular relaxation skills, often with the use of scientific instruments to monitor and inform the individual of his progress. This development, known as biofeedback, is helping millions of people to 'tune in' to their autonomic system and to take charge of it.

It must be emphasized that these ways of overcoming stress are vastly different to using alcohol, cigarettes, 'recreational' drugs, sleeping pills or tranquillizers. These substances can provide only temporary distraction, not long-lasting changes. All are addictive, some are known to cause serious health problems, such as liver damage and lung cancer, and others – particularly sleeping pills and tranquillizers – can leave the user feeling dazed or anaesthetised. Long-term users often hate their habit, but feel they can do nothing to change. They are hooked on the numbing effects and fear the pain of their ever-present tension. It makes sense, wherever possible, to introduce methods that deal with the stress instead of continuing to conceal it. Many people have been helped off tranquillizers and other drug use through learning relaxation methods.

Autogenic Training (AT)

Autogenic, which means self-generated, Training (AT) is a powerful psycho-physiological technique for relaxing the mind and body. It was originated by a doctor, Johannes Schultz, in Berlin at the turn of the century. He explored hypnosis and forms of Eastern meditation, and came to a synthesis of both in his approach.

Schultz's work was continued by Wolfgang Luthe, who

emigrated to Montreal in Canada, where he founded an International Institute for Stress and wrote six standard textbooks. Hans Selye, one of the best-known researchers into stress and its management, considered A T to be one of the best methods of stress control.

Dr Malcolm Carruthers was a London general practitioner when he became interested in stress-related illness. He trained with Luthe in Canada and then introduced A T to Britain, where it had a slow start but is gradually growing in demand.

A T is taught in group sessions, by doctors, psychologists or nurses who have undergone a one- or two-year training course. It is a passive technique, which Dr Carruthers insists is straightforward and 'like programming a computer'. The sequence of six standard exercises is taught in hour to hour-and-a-half long sessions once a week for eight weeks. The subject sits in a comfortable, relaxed upright position in an armchair, or slumps forward in the chair, which increases the range of situations in which A T can be used; or lies flat on his back. He concentrates on verbal instructions, given to a formula, focusing on relaxing sensations of heaviness, then warmth, in the arms and legs, a calm regular heart beat, an easy natural form of breathing, abdominal warmth and cooling of the forehead.

A certain discipline is involved in that the subject is supposed to practice A T in three to four ten-minute sessions a day. 'It has a high success rate – so long as you do it,' says Malcolm Carruthers. He claims that A T 'fortifies, restores and balances' the whole system, teaching you to 'switch off' the nervous system stimulation at will. Like physical training, though, the effects wear off if you lapse. 'It has to be as regular as brushing your teeth – look on it as brushing your brains.' It has been well tried, tested and documented and is used by anyone who wishes to improve his personal performance: groups have included executives, sports people, pilots. It also has clinical applications, such as in infertility and childbirth.

Basic AT groups are not suitable for people with serious psychological problems. This is not to suggest AT lacks power to help such cases, but means that it should be used in individual psychotherapy treatments where deep-seated problems will surface and be dealt with as part of a specialized AT 'neutralization' process.

Biofeedback

Biofeedback applies modern technology to the relaxation response. It entails monitoring and amplifying the neuro-physiological and other biological changes that occur when using simple relaxation methods, in order to recognize and bring them under more conscious control.

Biofeedback machines vary from basic hand-held ones, which may emit sounds of increasing pitch or use a simple dial to indicate rising stress, to complex measuring devices. In response to using any of the common relaxation methods, such as regularizing the breathing, the subject gains information about its effect on brain waves, heart rate, muscle tension, body temperature, stomach acidity or even white blood cell levels, according to the capacity of the device. He then learns to direct the method to elicit the required physiological response.

It is an infallible means of recognizing precise relationships between activity and response. Obviously, the more sophisticated and comprehensive the monitoring machinery, the better. For some people, learning to control their heart beat rate may not be as helpful in inducing complete relaxation as regulating muscle tension, for instance.

Biofeedback is best introduced by an instructor, but gradually the client learns how to switch on his relaxation response and use it in any situation.

Hypnotherapy

Hypnotherapy, the therapeutic application of hypnosis, has a melodramatic ring about it, but really is completely nonthreatening. Fears are based on stories of hypnosis inducing trances and of the subject putting himself in the power of the hypnotist – more scenes from a Victorian side-show than the modern therapy room.

Hypnotherapy does alter brainwave patterns, but no more than in any other state of deep relaxation. And although it relies to some extent on suggestibility, it has been demonstrated that clients remain enough in charge of their functioning to be able to come out of the hypnosis at any time. No reputable therapist would misuse his authority by doing anything other than meeting the client's stated needs. Hypnotherapy is a way of programming the unconscious mind. You should make clear before the therapy begins whether you want it for general stress reduction or for dealing with specific stress-related situations, like fear of flying. The therapist will be able to make relevant suggestions, which become more easily incorporated into your psychology while you are in the deeply relaxed state. At the end of a session the hypnotherapist will gently bring the subject back to full consciousness feeling refreshed and alert, as if waking from a deep sleep.

Sometimes just one session can make long-held tensions disappear. Often, however, regular sessions are needed for some months, as it can take time to enter the experience fully and learn to let go and trust the therapist. It has been said that some people make better hypnotherapy subjects than others, but the main requirement is a desire to participate.

Meditation

Meditation methods have always been part of Eastern

philosophy. They are considered the only way to detach from the thought processes, which carry with them the seeds of stress. Meditation is based on non-doing, on ceasing identification with unnecessary disturbances and allowing the body, mind and breath to settle naturally. The meditative state has several levels, traditionally leading to complete enlightenment. While not generally requiring themselves to attain these heights, most Westerners are happy with tranquillity and calm attentiveness as a first stage.

Meditation usually entails sitting in a comfortable posture, preferably one that helps you stay awake. To this end, the back should be kept straight. You then concentrate on an object or sound (known as a 'mantra'). A pattern, colour or just your own breathing are also acceptable. The point is to dwell without strain or tension on the chosen focus, bringing the mind back to open awareness and contemplation whenever it strays – as it naturally will. In time the mind will empty of extraneous thought and you will become calmer and have greater charge of your own processes.

There are many schools of meditation, but the basic practice is common to all. A familiar method in the West is Transcendental Meditation (TM), which is a good introduction to this most ancient relaxation method.

Progressive relaxation

This is a method of learning deep muscular relaxation, based on Benson's 'relaxation response' (see p. 135). It is learned as a skill, just as you would learn to ride a bicycle or swim, and is often incorporated into yoga classes. It is called progressive because it relaxes muscles and muscle groups in sequence, from feet up to head.

Progressive relaxation is done in a comfortable, lying down position, in a warm room without distractions. The usual method is purposely to contract the major muscles and then relax them. The relaxation will be deeper than before the imposed contraction, and in time you will be able to sense where tension accumulates and when it is not properly discharged. Regular practice will enable you to recognize which parts of the body are most affected by daily stresses and it becomes second nature to deal with them. You can, for example, forestall driving strain and even face the dentist with impunity.

The method is immensely flexible. Main sessions, where you get to know your body and its stresses, can be conducted in any quiet few moments at home, and it can be applied at any time in any situation, whenever you turn your mind to it.

Personal view

● *Jenny, 33, senior veterinary nurse.* I originally did an autogenic training course a few years ago because I was getting very wound up at work, dealing with hysterical people, angry dogs, three telephones and all the staff. I heard about autogenic training through a client, but I was already interested in relaxation and knew it was a real key to surviving.

At the time I felt I was heading right down the drain. I realized if I didn't slow down, I'd give myself a nervous breakdown, I don't think I would have coped at all. I know it sounds dramatic, but autogenic training changed my life. I never could have imagined myself saying that about anything, but it made such a difference.

I did find it difficult at first, I was running round in circles and it was hard to set aside the time to do it. But it made me see how little space I was willing to give myself and I feel it stopped me in my tracks a bit. Gradually I slowed down and changed myself; my boyfriend said the difference in me was incredible.

I even went back to do the course a second time, not because I desperately needed to but because I wanted to, for fun. I found it even more helpful the second time. It was an all-women group and really nice. I don't think it's essential to repeat the course – once is plenty because that gives you the basis for doing as much as you want.

I do some every day, even though I'm very lazy, in sessions anything from five minutes to half an hour, which I try to do more than once a day. If I think I haven't got the time, I lock myself in the loo. The more I do, the more I get out of it.

Where to go

Autogenic Training

Positive Health Centre
101 Harley Street
London W1
Tel: 01-935-1811

Biofeedback, meditation

Audio Ltd
26–28 Wendell Road
London W12 9RT
Tel: 01-743-1518

Hypnotherapy

Association for Applied
Hypnosis
33 Abbey Park Road
Grimsby, South
Humberside DN32 OHS
Tel: 0472–47702

Association of Hypnotists
and Psychotherapists
25 Market Square
Nelson, Lancashire
BB9 7LP
Tel: 0282-699378

Association of
Qualified Curative
Hypnotherapists
10 Balaclava Road
Kings Heath,
Birmingham B14 7SG
Tel: 021-444-5435

British Society of
Hypnotherapists
51 Queen Anne Street
London W1M 9FA
Tel: 01-935-7075

Meditation

National Centre for
Transcendental
Meditation
Roydon Hall
Seven Mile Lane
East Peckham
Tonbridge, Kent
TN12 5NH
Tel: 0622-813243

General

Relaxation for Living
29 Burwood Park Road
Walton-on-Thames,
Surrey KT12 5LH

What is it?

Rolfers claim they can alter physical structure. Their ten-session system of intense connective tissue manipulation, combined with movement education, reorganizes the basic 'blocks', or areas, of the body into alignment much as you would balance bricks to create a firm structure. To do so they use knuckles, elbows, fingers and forearms in a massage-like action that works deeply into the tissue.

Ida Rolf, originator of the system, called her work Structural Integration. She talked of the human body in terms of integration or disorganization, symmetry or random movement. Faults in a disorganized body affect every part of it. For example a forward tilting pelvis deepens the curve of the lower spine, the rib cage compensates by inclining backwards and the head by jutting outwards, and consequently the upper chest is flattened and the breathing shortened.

The distortion does not have to be extreme. A shoulder may be lifted almost imperceptibly except to the trained eye, the foot tilted so that the shoe heel wears down on one side only. Observing the whole body as it moves, one may see the unequal pace of separate parts, the trunk seeming to work harder than the legs, or the head pitching into space. What passes for normal is within all of these limits; rarely do we see the human body working as a harmonious unity.

The problem, according to Ida Rolf, is that we are at war with gravity. Each time an area of the body slips out of alignment, the whole structure is weakened and at the mercy of attack by the downward pull. The building brick analogy says it all: should one small section of a building shift or bulge, the whole edifice is in danger of sliding into a pile of rubble. In contrast, a well-integrated body will stand firm with the beauty, symmetry and strength of a time-defying piece of architecture. This is the aim of Rolfing: to get all sections of the body working with equal balance and comfort so that it is held effortlessly within gravity.

Because of this vision of the body, Rolfing originally was considered mainly a therapy for people with physical problems. Gradually, however, it has also gained a reputation as an adjunct to psychotherapy. The deep physical release it affords as the segments of the body are rebuilt and learn to relate and integrate often initiates psychological and emotional change. Rolfer Harvey Burns explains, 'It's all to do with how people physically handle their emotions and feelings, as well as the other things like direct impact. With emotional things, it's as if some of the power behind the trauma is locked away into the body tissue. So if someone's shoulders are slumped and drawn forward in a continual attitude of defeat and sadness which they have had since a child, that compression in their bodies was how they handled and contained that feeling so it didn't overwhelm them.'

Emotional factors and physical injury also interact. Says Harvey Burns: 'An area which starts off as the centre of some kind of emotional holding will have a predisposition to being a key area and so if the person gets ill or is injured, it will probably affect that part first. Even if we grow out of the initial feelings which set up the tension, the tissue is still set that way and will be prone to things going wrong.'

Fascia, the essential connection

Rolfers physically restructure the body by working on the

fascia, one of the basic elements that support and hold the body together. This connective tissue covers the whole body under the skin rather like a thin but very strong elastic body stocking, and runs around the muscles and between muscle groups, dividing them functionally so that they can work individually. Its one outstanding characteristic is elasticity. Because it is elastic, fascia changes in response to mechanical demands. The misalignment of parts of the body, whether from emotional dramas or physical injuries, distorts the fascia, shortening or thickening it. A certain kind of applied pressure – the technique of Rolfing – can loosen the fascia, restoring its elasticity and freeing the parts of the body so they can be realigned. Ida Rolf said, 'Connective tissues are in a never-ending state of reorganization. The continuous metabolic interchange made possible through the intimate relation of fascia with water metabolism allows structural reorganization.'

Rolfers often experience fascia under their hands as a hard, thickened, gristly sheet of tissue. 'But as we work on it, it palpably begins to feel softer, more loose and fluid,' says Harvey Burns. Rolfing regards this fluidity as the essential condition of the body, and the art is to regenerate the living, moving plasticity in place of rigidity and obstruction.

Although the technique is directed to the fascia, Harvey Burns hesitates to pigeon-hole Rolfing as connective tissue work. 'The truth is that in the living body functionally things are inseparable. Muscles are surrounded by and interwoven with fascia, which then reaches the end of the muscle and becomes tendon, which then goes into bone. In real life you cannot see where one starts and one finishes. Bones, muscles, fascia, tendons, ligaments, they are all integrated units.' In Rolfing the fascia is really a way into dealing with all these and everything that they influence. As Ida Rolf said, 'Fascia forms an intricate web coextensive with the body, central to the body, central to its well-being, central to its performance. Clearly, fascial tone, fascial span, is a basic contributing factor to bodily well-being.'

Ida Rolf

Ida Rolf was an American biochemist, who was driven by the determination to do something practical for people who no one else could help, whether it was a friend with a sprained ankle, another crippled after a childhood fall or her own somewhat sickly son.

Many of her ideas about the human body, especially the basic one that structure determines function, were influenced by osteopathy, which she experienced both as a patient and student. A strong and forthright woman, she talked in practical terms about what the therapist could get his hands on. 'Stop thinking and get to work' was her attitude. Nevertheless, her work embraces a wider view. 'We must see man as an energy field, rather than a mass of matter; a field which lives within a greater energy field, the field of Earth,' she said. Failure to recognize this interaction of forces, she believed, led to a sense of insecurity, aggression and fear.

Ida Rolf was not given to extravagant claims about the technique's effects. 'We are interested,' she said, 'in making a more adequate body for men and women so they can disregard the problems of the body and stick to the things they want to stick to – their job or their sports. We don't set out to "cure" a body. But we get that body to grow to a place of greater strength and adaptability, greater grace in movement and greater capacity for moving and adjusting.'

What to expect

Ten sessions are basic to Rolfing, but one or two more are given when necessary. Some people, too, may need one or two 'top-up' sessions six months to a year afterwards to help the body integrate the effects. This is largely left up to the individual, although the Rolfer sometimes suggests a client comes back. 'We bring the body to a point of balance and then in another few months see if they need more, which some people do, and a lot of people don't,' says Harvey Burns.

Rolfers use slow, deep movements, dictated by the pace of the client's own body rhythms. It is the combination of their controlled body weight behind the hand pressure, hand heat and the energetic interchange between Rolfer and client that changes the tissue from its semi-solid, gluey state to a more fluid one. 'All this has a profound effect,' explains Harvey Burns, 'because if you push and poke with your muscle power, or address connective tissue sharply or rub, it tends to react. But if you get pressure and pace just right, there can be a really deep release.' The use of balanced body weight means the Rolfer often gets into some rather strange positions, perhaps getting up on the broad Rolfing table beside the client in order to use his own body efficiently.

The client experiences a deep, kneading massage. There is no hiding the fact that Rolfing is sometimes very painful: fascia set in its ways can feel as tight as steel cables and nothing less than determined pressure will soften it. The Rolfer's stroke can seem unrelenting, yet his sensitivity enables him to judge just how far to go. The client learns to relax and breathe with the pressure and thus assist the releasing process; Rolfer and client work together. Tensing against pain is sometimes inevitable, but will not help.

Often the Rolfer will stop short of completing a process

to let the client appreciate the work that has been done, by comparing the freedom and sense of elongation on one side of the body with the restricted and foreshortened movement on the other. Whatever area has been involved in each session, the spine and neck receive attention as a finishing touch.

Rolfing sessions are usually weekly. The first one can last up to two hours; thereafter, sessions take from an hour to an hour and a half. Each has a predetermined structure and aim, but enough flexibility to allow for emotional catharsis, individual needs and, possibly, discussion.

Before work begins in session 1, photographs of the client from the front, back and both sides are usually taken. This is also the session in which Rolfer and client get used to each other and establish a rapport, which is necessary before deeper work can go on.

The work in this session is primarily concerned with the superficial fascia. It focuses on the upper chest, shoulder girdle and hips and aims at making breathing, often restricted as a reaction to stress, fuller and more efficient. This is significant for the whole body: Ida Rolf maintained that changing someone's breathing could effect changes at a cellular level since the increased uptake of oxygen affects overall health.

Session 2 concentrates on the lower legs, feet and back, creating space round the ankle and heel, each toe and all the tiny ligaments. Language is full of metaphors for what this session is trying to achieve: 'He's got his feet on the ground.' 'He's well balanced,' 'He can stand up for himself.' Rolfers see how clients have tried, almost literally, to sink down into the ground or to lift themselves away from it. The work aims at balancing the body mass on the ground, increasing the sense of squareness and firmness.

Session 3 is concerned with opening up the sides of the body along the hips, rib cage, upper arm and neck. Rolfing may reveal compensatory stress patterns; a displacement at the knee, say, can cause zigzags of locked fascia at alternate positions along each side. It is common for one side to be softer, more pliable and less resistant than the other.

In session 4 the Rolfer works on the inside of the calves and thighs, with the ultimate aim of freeing the pelvis from below. Often legs become shortened and not firm enough to support the weight above. Conversely, all the weight may be concentrated here, dragging the pelvic area with it. In both cases the pelvis will become held in and restricted, the legs feel stiff and the whole effect be of disunited parts.

In session 5 the work concentrates on the abdomen and the deep structures therein. It too relates to the pelvis, this time aiming to release it from above. Often this session has deep emotional content as the gut is the traditional seat of the emotions and where people hold in anger, sadness and pain. When a client has problems to do with birth (her own or that of a child) or conception, or feels full of suppressed rage, this is the area where the Rolfer expects to find tightness.

Session 6 is concerned with the complete back of the body from heels right up to the head. To the Rolfer a tight back can denote someone who tends to 'hold back'.

In session 7 the Rolfer works on the head, neck, face and jaw, which, like the abdomen, are prime places for holding. As a result, the neck, for example, may be hard to move without involving unnecessary movement in other parts of the body. The face often holds lots of emotional tension, and Rolfers work inside the mouth with gloved fingers. Here may be felt more intensely than anywhere what Rolfing tries to achieve – a sense of cavernous extra space – because of the special sensitivity of the area.

The last three sessions work on integrating the parts of the loosened body into a new structure and new patterns of movement. The Rolfer must decide what is most ap-

Rolfing's results are clearly illustrated in these 'before' and 'after' pictures from photographs of a man in his late sixties.

propriate to the client's needs, working on balancing upper and lower parts of the body, with extra attention to any stumbling blocks that still resist integration. Some areas may not be completely softened, but it is enough that taut tissue is beginning to release throughout the body. Final photographs are taken to contrast with those taken before the Rolfing began.

Although changes occur throughout the Rolfing process, Rolfers point out that the process of adjustment continues for up to a year after completion of the ten sessions. The most obvious and immediate changes are usually dramatic improvements in posture: the behind less protruding, loss of excess spinal curve, head better balanced on the neck, reduction in round-shoulderedness and a taller appearance. The range of movement is wider and freer, and there is a new ease and sense of well-being. Breathing changes and there is more energy and the whole system works better. In fact, Rolfers believe that because less demand is being put on the system, the rate of entropy, or slowing down, usually associated with ageing is much reduced. People have a better self-image, they like the way they look. This sets up a positive cycle – because they look better, they feel better and are able to relax.

After the obvious and immediate, changes may continue less noticeably as people adjust gradually. 'One of the things that happens when body balance alters is that the nervous system is thrown into slight disarray. There is a period in which your nervous system is aware that things aren't as they were before. People experience this as feeling that something is changing. After a while the nervous system gets the message that this is where things are going to be, because they have been released, and it will slowly re-programme the messages and they will become part of the new situation,' explains Harvey Burns. You may not feel anything happening – but it is.

At its most successful, Rolfing will point the whole being in the direction of continued development. 'There can be profound enough change to set the person on a route that becomes positive and progressive rather than negative and deteriorating,' says Harvey Burns. Whether that happens has everything to do with the individual's willingness to take on the process of change for himself, using the opening of awareness begun on a physical level. He explains:

Once the body has opened up, and we come to look at
some of our physical, emotional, behavioural and social
patterns with awareness and clarity, this is the

beginning of the journey. You can open up a person's body so their whole way of presenting themselves is more open. But if they are not prepared to handle what that means, have the courage to become that new, open, alive person, the work is going to go much slower. If they have the commitment and interest, they usually explore that new self a little and then refer back to the old, and then re-evaluate, experiment again and so on – that process can continue for the rest of your life.

The early Rolfers believed it was not their job to handle emotional catharsis. Today, however, most Rolfers are interested in this level of release and deal with it as part of the sessions. Where tight fascia owes its origins to severe emotional trauma, it can help if feelings are discharged. Such traumas become physically locked into the body tissue because it was somehow unacceptable to express the relevant emotions at the time they occurred. Releasing the physical pressure can cause people to experience some of the emotional charge that originally locked them into that position.

However, emotional catharsis is certainly neither expected nor necessary for the success of the therapy. Even people who touch no deep-held emotions during Rolfing feel positive results nevertheless. 'Once tissue has been released it's not going to seize up again. It just can't do that,' affirms Harvey Burns. 'Although there might be a tendency to go back to the old patterns, they would be functional not structural. Often, some simple massage or exercise will release them again.'

Who benefits?

Rolfing attracts many kinds of people. There are those already involved in some kind of personal growth therapy, who see this as one more way of piecing together different aspects of themselves; artistic people, wishing to increase their flexibility and sensitivity to enhance their self-expression; sports people and others requiring peak physical performance levels, people in pain and those who have never recovered from injury; and those who are interested in posture and movement in general. Individual practitioners find they attract the kind of person they work best with.

Related therapies

Rolfing has given rise to many developments and variations. Although adequate treatments in their own right Hellerwork, Postural Integration and Rebalancing have a direct line of descent from Rolfing.

Hellerwork

Hellerwork is a series of eleven 90-minute sessions developed by Joseph Heller and based to a large degree on Rolfing, and aims not just to realign the body but also to educate the client in maintaining flexibility after completing the sessions. Like Rolfing, it focuses on the body's essential fluidity and plasticity and uses the practitioner's body weight and technique to work on fascia so that the whole structure becomes better balanced. Joseph Heller explains, 'In optimal condition, fascia is a loose, moist tissue. When there is continual loose movement and balance in the body, the fascial body stocking stays loose and mobile, facilitating the movement between different parts of the body. However, under continual stress and lack of movement fascia becomes rigid and loses its fluidity. Although people most often associate tension and stiffness with their muscles, it is actually the connective tissue that accumulates much of this stress.'

The eleven sessions, Heller says, are like 'peeling an onion'. They are divided into three groups. One to three focus on the superficial fascia layer and may also deal with issues of infancy and childhood – standing up and reaching out. Sessions four to seven are called 'core' sessions, and address the deeper-lying tissue that assists fine motor mechanisms and must be used in order to produce graceful, fluid movement. They may also relate to adolescent feelings: control and surrender, holding back, intellectual development. Eight to eleven are integrating sessions. They follow no set course, but seek to align the unique patterns of the individual client and may help him focus on his life as a mature adult: integrating masculinity and femininity, finding his place in the world. No bodywork is done in the final session. It is a time for discussing what has gone before and making sure the client feels able to use what he has gained.

In bodywork Hellerworkers, who are trained in a very 'career-orientated' American system, use energy and concentration to ease out the fascia. They may use elbows and knuckles to get right down to the deep underlying tissue, and claim the technique is more gentle than Rolfing, while reaching just as deeply. As with Rolfing, 'melting' into the pressure is the best way for the client to deal with it.

Any permanent change, Hellerworkers maintain, comes though making the client aware of how he is using his body in simple everyday movements. 'If the bodywork aspect of Hellerwork is like taking the dents out of a car's bumper after the car has run into a tree,' says Joseph Heller, 'then movement education can be likened to re-educating the driver so that he won't continue to destroy his vehicle. No amount of removing dents will keep a car beautiful if the driver is continually hitting trees.'

Suggestions and visualizations play a large part in showing the client what has been amiss in his body use. Any particular interests, like hobbies, sports or job activities, are taken into account, with the therapist suggesting how these may be done with less restriction and greater ease.

The aspect of Hellerwork labelled 'verbal dialogue' concentrates on the emotions. The physical theme of each session highlights the attitudes most often associated with that area of the body. In the first session, for example, which deals with the chest – the area of the heart – the emotional focus is on inspiration. The therapist may ask questions such as 'Do you feel inspired?' 'What inspires you?' The process is designed to increase awareness of feelings and emotional charge, and how the tension associated with them has become impacted into the tissue. As physical tension is released, emotional patterns can begin to dissolve, aided by heightened awareness, which is a catalyst for change.

The goal of Hellerwork is to reverse the pattern of self-limitation, in which posture and self-expression become locked up together. Instead, says Joseph Heller, they can 'become a different kind of team, each assisting one another to unwind'. Ultimately this process must be the client's responsibility. Thus the final session ensures the client is able to release tension and bring balance back into his own body. As Joseph Heller says, 'In the future, you may want to use your practitioner as a resource, but, primarily, responsibility for your physical well-being lies with you, as it always did.'

Postural integration

This is another form of deep bodywork. While its 'mother' is Rolfing, its 'father' could be said to be Reichian bodywork, or bioenergetics (see pp. 63–74). It was started by an American, Jack Painter, a philosophy professor, who became interested in bodywork during the 1960s. He was Rolfed but needed to go further, since Rolfing at the time was limited to physical structure and working on the fascia. Eventually, after exploring many forms of physical and emotional release prevalent in California at the time, he adapted the work of Ida Rolf to incorporate more gentle techniques and a more emotional cathartic focus.

Therapist Silke Ziehl calls Postural Integration 'an intense journey of self-exploration. It is like a powerful drug – you only give it to those who can cope physically and emotionally.' For that reason it is important for prospective client and therapist to meet and interview each other, to find out if they can work together.

Sessions last two hours, and a course of ten or twelve is usual. First comes a 'body reading', in which the client, undressed as far as is comfortable, is observed by the therapist, who gains a 'feel' for the kind of tensions held in the body. At the same time the client plays his part, being invited towards a deeper understanding of his body by experiencing, perhaps for the first time, exactly what he is doing with it. Silke Ziehl asks questions like, 'What are you aware of that's happening in your body now?' 'What is happening in your feet?' 'Are you aware of what you are doing to your knees?' Where some attitude catches the attention, she asks the client to exaggerate it, and to express any feelings. Thus a deep emotional connection is made with what the body does.

'Where does your breath go?' is another question of prime importance. 'Most of the time breathing is constricted in most people,' explains Silke Ziehl. 'But the breathing carries everything. If it can be made to flow more appropriately, energy follows.' Because people find the concept of energy flow rather abstract, she tells them to think in terms of the breath's direction, and that creates a direct consciousness of which areas are cut off from this vitalizing force.

Postural Integration sees breath flow as flexible and variable. 'It is unnatural to encourage the breath to be even all the time,' Silke Ziehl points out. She asks people to experiment in sessions with breathing in many different ways and paces, imagining it going down the spine or into the sides and seeing how much breath they can handle. This encourages spontaneity and breathing rhythms that flow with emotion instead of stopping it. Invariably, change in physical structure follows as the energy is released.

In the second part of the session the client lies down and the therapist tries to release rigidity from connective tissue by a variety of means. She may put one hand on an area where there is little movement, she may bring forth laughter if the client tends to be straightlaced or calm a surface 'buzz' that seems to drain energy from other areas.

At the end of each session the therapist and client allow the energy system time to change and continue experiencing what they can discover about emotional patterns through what the tissue, quite literally, 'embodies'.

Rather like Rolfing, each session may deal with specific areas, but from a different standpoint. A session on the arms, for example, will try to make the client aware of what he is reaching out towards, what he is asking for. While working on the chest, he may have to come to terms with what he wants to 'get off his chest', or express. Other areas of exploration are what he does with feelings of vulnerability, or whereabouts anger is stored. The relationship of feelings and body is centrally clarified until the client sees that the two are constantly interacting and understands what that means to him as an individual.

Rebalancing

Rebalancing uses the deep tissue massage of Rolfing, but comes from a slightly different philosophy. It is influenced by the thinking of Bhagwan Shri Rajneesh, an Indian teacher who has had considerable effect on many Western spiritual seekers. At his ashram, or community, in Poona, India (and also, briefly, in America) he has synthesized classical Eastern philosophy with the modern psychological methods of the West. Some people see him as a controversial, cult figure, but there is no doubt he has given many a powerful spiritual focus and the tools for self-development.

Rajneesh's philosophy is based on non-thinking, allowing the body's energy to flow spontaneously until you are so integrated with yourself and your surroundings that you fall into a state of oneness, or meditation. Here is what he has to say about rebalancing: 'Touch is one of the most forgotten languages ... when you touch the body of a person, flow with total energy. And whenever you see the body flowing and the energy creating a new pattern of harmony, you will feel a delight that you have never felt before. You will fall into deep meditation.'

Rebalancer Neerjo Sieker explains, 'Rebalancing includes this dimension of love, trust and meditation that is so central to Rajneesh's work. The difference from Rolfing is that it sees the need for something more than just the physical work. It adds a spiritual quality to life.'

A rebalancing session takes between one and a half and two hours. The number of sessions is flexible: one session can be complete in itself, but if a person can come for a series, so much the better.

First the rebalancer will take an assessing look at the standing body, mentally noting imbalances in the structure. The work then covers every area of the body with kneading and pummelling action, as in Rolfing. Tense, sensitive areas are given especial treatment. Stiff muscles in buttocks, shoulders and arms are coaxed into giving way. 'We are transmitting the idea to the tissue that it can let go and still be all right,' says Neerjo. Sometimes it is painful, but shows definite results.

There are also some softer, more gentle strokes and a relaxing, shaking movement of limbs and torso. The use of the breath is much in evidence: the therapist may pant gently and swiftly to maintain his vital energy flow. He will also be listening carefully for the breathing rhythms of the client, and harmonizing his actions with them. There is a clear sense of communication and empathy.

As the name suggests, there is indeed a remarkable sensation of becoming balanced and integrated. Changes seem to occur on many levels simultaneously. Rebalancers say that during the physical process of the therapy comes a corresponding change in the client's thought and attitudes, due to the freeing of life energy, or vibration. 'It gives a feeling of unity and integrity. The person develops grace in movement and a corresponding psychological attitude of being graceful. The result is a person whose movement and behaviour have a high grade of spontaneity and yet is still coordinated and effective – the quality of natural grace. People are fully alive, with a clear radiance.'

Perhaps most important, rebalancing makes you aware of your tensions and helps you learn how to breathe and relax into deeper and deeper layers of your body, without blocking what is there. This self-treatment continues outside the therapy session; in fact, rebalancing is only the beginning. 'Sinking into yourself, you can bring out your fear, sorrow or anger or you can be very still,' says Neerjo. 'Rebalancing takes you beyond relaxation to a state of joyful stillness.'

Personal views

● *Bernard, 43, musician.* I was Rolfed ten years ago,
when I was working as a drummer and percussionist
in the United States. I had started having some
massage, which highlighted that my body was a little
bit stiff and a little bit frozen from years of playing
drums and also from a few car accidents. I trusted this
masseuse, so when she told me to go and have some
Rolfing, I did, and the results were amazing.

The change in my body was so remarkable and so
noticeable, particularly because I already used it every
day in an artistic way. I noticed I could do much more
complex things physically with much less strain. It was
as if I discovered my body's natural momentum, so the
amount of muscle effort I had to use to perform a
particular piece was much less. I found my playing
improved incredibly, with about half as much energy
output, which was enormously satisfying because it
gave me much more chance to be expressive
emotionally.

Also, in my everyday life my body felt so much more
open and free in the way it moved, even in walking.
Again, I felt I was using less effort and energy to
perform very simple tasks. When relieved of that kind
of strain and clumsiness I experienced a sense of
aliveness and well-being that I didn't think I was ever
going to have again. I thought it was just something
you had as a child and as you got older that was it, it
went. Instead I rediscovered this incredible looseness
and vitality.

I'd always thought of myself as a bookish kind of
person, because I'd never enjoyed physical things at
school. I suddenly realized that I was a physical type

after all, but I hadn't allowed myself to explore it when I was growing up because I hadn't enjoyed the feeling of being in my body. I realized I really did enjoy having a body, it was a wonderful revelation to me, and I started running and swimming and doing yoga.

Almost everything improved. I relaxed, my voice changed, I really felt I was beginning to become more myself. It was like all the old baggage dropping away and I felt 'me' starting to come out; it was a very satisfying experience. My sex life improved, my relationships with other people improved – apart from a few which disappeared altogether because I started to express a lot of anger that had been stored up. But it was all very positive and it was a turning point for me. I still experience my body changing in a positive direction even though I only had those few sessions all that time ago.

● *Andrea, 33, journalist.* People had warned me Rolfing was painful and that worried me at first, but it was only a problem in two of the sessions. My upper arms and around my calves and thighs were the worst, and there I did have difficulty releasing the tension within myself as the Rolfer was working on me.

The sessions varied very much for me. There were times when I came away with a sense of lightness and well-being, release and expansion, which was somehow more than just being relaxed but a deeper awareness. Often there was this feeling of being easier, light and unburdened, warmer and carefree, as if I was running on little oiled wheels. Other times I was shaky and tired, particularly when it had been a difficult and painful session. After the leg work I was really shivering and in touch with the tension under my skin.

Psychologically, too, I went through traumas about

being inadequate, at having stored up so much tension while believing I was perfectly fine and relaxed, and feeling a failure when I resisted the process and would not, or could not, help the Rolfer get rid of all this locked-up pain. I went through a lot of sadness and depression during and between the sessions, which I discussed with my Rolfer although I didn't actually emote all over her.

There were times when everything seemed to go smoothly and easily, and then suddenly there were what seemed like great blocks of my body where nothing could be shifted. Even when I didn't feel a sense of release and was disappointed or felt we needed longer, my Rolfer calmly told me things were happening and her aims had been achieved.

At the end I could see from the before and after photos that subtle changes had taken place. I held my head higher and my face was looking more directly to the front. My expression was more open and soft. My shoulders had expanded and widened and seemed to have moved back slightly, and the area under my shoulder blades was no longer so contracted. People remarked that I looked taller and more poised and that my back was nice and straight.

Six months later, I must say I am not aware of any major changes, and I do feel I have gone back to my old patterns to some extent. But I have a greater awareness of how I use my body and know when I am holding on to my shoulders or hiding my face; the tension in my legs though remains hard for me to shift.

Where to go

Rolfing

Harvey Burns
80 Clifton Hill
London NW8 0JT
Tel: 01-328-9026

Pru Rankin-Smith
61 Grantham Road
London W4 2RT
Tel: 01-994-8544

Hellerwork

Institute of Structural
Bodywork
8 Cervantes Court
Ruston Mews
London W11 1UE
Tel: 01-243-0132

Postural Integration

Centre for Release and
Integration
14 Glamorgan Road
Hampton Wick
Kingston upon Thames,
Surrey KT1 4HP
Tel: 01-977-2226

Rebalancing

71 Anson Road
Tufnell Park
London N7 0AS
Tel: 01-609-2525

T'AI-CHI

What is it?

T'ai-chi is an ancient art of movement meditation: a spiritual, mental and physical discipline. Originating in China, it forms at its simplest level the obligatory early morning exercise routine practised by millions of Chinese daily as the standard means to health. In the West it has been popular for about thirty years.

T'ai-chi looks like a slow, deliberate dance. The movements are flowing and based on a circular pattern. There is constant motion for the full half hour or so it takes to perform the complete sequence, always with poise, control and intense concentration. At its best, t'ai-chi performance imparts a sense of almost supernatural fluidity, a completely effortless shifting from high to low, from reaching outward to returning within. It illustrates a harmonious way of being, which can be taken to whatever levels the practitioner requires.

There are two major schools of thought on t'ai-chi. One puts it firmly among the martial arts and denies it has any profound esoteric significance or is a means of spiritual development. The movements are done simply for their physical benefits – as in China – or for practical self-defence. Since however the martial arts rely on obtaining mastery over the *chi*, or energy force, studying t'ai-chi even at this physical level entails some relationship with unseen forces that can lead to a spiritual dimension.

The other way of looking at t'ai-chi is as a fundamental

T'ai-chi movements have immense grace and fluidity.

tool for altering perception through understanding the significance of the movements in terms of Chinese philosophy, and by mastering the movements and giving to them an inner, individual meaning that is both creative and inspirational, thus treating the t'ai-chi as an art form.

The name t'ai-chi suggests the martial arts connection:

one translation is 'supreme ultimate fist'. As one teacher, Beverley Milne, points out, however, the fist can also be interpreted as a container of energy and not necessarily an aggressive force. The word *ch'üan*, often added, simply means exercises, and *t'ai-chi-ch'üan* may be translated loosely as 'exercises for self-mastery'.

Origins and philosophy of t'ai-chi

The beginnings of t'ai-chi are shrouded in history, and obscured by fantasy. It is generally believed to date from the eleventh century, when a man called Chang San-feng, born of a noble family, went into the army and there learned the exercises currently given for self-defence and general health. On leaving the army, he felt the need for some higher philosophical or spiritual discipline to be applied to the fighting techniques. He developed this principle, introducing the ideas of chivalry, compassion, brotherhood and unity and giving underlying meaning to the purely physical movements.

This amalgamation of martial arts exercise with spiritual discipline was developed further in Chinese Taoist and Buddhist monasteries and temple schools, when elements of the 'preventive medicine' practised by the monks were added until it gradually became the practice known today. For a long time it was regarded in the East as an esoteric pursuit. Eventually, its masterful techniques were adopted by the army and hence the more martial aspects came to the fore.

At its deepest level t'ai-chi incorporates basic Taoist (Tao is pronounced 'dow' and means 'the way') philosophy, which lies at the roots of ancient Chinese civilization. Taoism recognizes that everything in the universe – not only the animal, vegetable and mineral kingdoms, but also invisible energetic elements – is part of an interpenetrating unity. Man himself is a microcosm, a miniature universe, and everything that happens externally is reflected in his body and psyche.

However, these elements are not locked in an indivisible symbiosis. The unity of the universe consists of a constant blending and changing, an ebb and flow and the interplay of opposites that attract and repel. The role of the human being is to adapt and flow with the whole of life, rather than struggling to exert his own will against the odds. In letting go and surrendering to the greater unity, he will become stronger than by actively resisting life's movement, said the Taoists, using metaphors from nature to illustrate the point: the branch of a tree bending under the weight of snow but not breaking; a stream of water dividing to pass a rock then flowing as one again. These natural laws are fundamental to the Taoist discipline; we resist them at the risk of tension, disharmony and mental and physical illness. T'ai-chi's movements became expressions of the Tao in action. Thus a firm, dynamic outward movement flows into one that is yielding and receptive. Says Beverley Milne: 'If you study the t'ai-chi, you can find the whole Taoist perception of thought, feeling, soul and spirit – all in a nutshell. Then the purpose of doing it becomes healing and whole-making.'

Milne and other t'ai-chi teachers believe that understanding this philosophy is central to the teaching of t'ai-chi. Even though its roots go back thousands of years, its principle of flowing with life's circumstances makes it entirely suitable today. Not only does it give a complete world view, but it also relates to our internal self, our psychology. 'Just talking about Chinese philosophy is not enough,' explains Beverley Milne. 'Everything has to be related to the now. When you see the t'ai-chi as a total working, it is like a self-analysis. It shows people how their thoughts and emotions come out through physical expression. But teaching body language is not enough. Working with the t'ai-chi becomes a spiritual training. By harmonizing thought and feeling through the body you become a unified personality.'

The person attributed with bringing t'ai-chi to England in the 1950s is Gerda Geddes, a dancer, psychoanalyst and movement teacher who was struck by its integrated approach to breath, balance and movement. Although at the time t'ai-chi was considered an exclusively male pursuit, Geddes eventually persuaded a Chinese t'ai-chi master to teach it to her by the traditional means of allowing her silent, meditative mirroring.

To her disappointment, t'ai-chi was initially unenthusiastically received in England. Following t'ai-chi's philosophical teaching, to cease fighting and flow with life's lessons, though, she found an immediate change: an upsurge of interest and an influx of pupils.

The form of t'ai-chi

Form means the 100 or so movements of the t'ai-chi, which take about thirty minutes to perform. (There is also a short form of thirty-seven movements, but this is an American version condemned by purists.) The sequence is precise and unvarying. It is usually done in the 'Yang' style, named after the Chinese practitioner who popularized it. This style's major characteristic is an upright spine. All the movements are carried out with relaxation and tranquillity. The weight is kept mainly on one foot, which entails shifting in a graceful swaying motion, keeping a central balance and alignment. The spine is held as if suspended, the chin kept in and the knees, usually kept flexed, point in the same direction as the toes.

To the newcomer, one of t'ai-chi's most memorable aspects is the imaginative naming of movements, such as Strumming the Lute; Embrace Tiger, Return to Mountain;

Searching for the Needle at the Bottom of the Sea. While such names can be taken as literal descriptions, many teachers see them as allegories of the spiritual quest. Beverley Milne teaches that the 'needle' is the eye of the spirit; the 'sea' is the wellspring of wisdom, the 'tiger' is personal energy; and the 'mountain' represents stillness and rest.

Strum the Lute is one example of how movement that reflects a simple activity can also symbolize the Taoist philosophy. With the fist clenched, the creative energy is at the ready, yet shielded and protected as it waits. At the same time the foot stays to one side, without moving forward. There is a pause to consolidate, integrate and rest. When the time is right, the way is open to go forward and release energy to do what is required. At that point there is a directed movement forward and a twist, with the palm opening and turning away as the leg is released, symbolizing an emptying of resistance.

The breath is important. Each movement 'rides on the breath', as Beverley Milne puts it. The timing depends on the individual's metabolism and while one person may take less than twenty-five minutes to complete the form (although it should not be speeded up much more than this), another may take more than half an hour.

T'ai-chi should never be a slavish repetition. Its basic form is a key for personal interpretation. 'It is an evolving art and everybody will give it their different, personal flavour, not deliberately or as an imposition but according to how they are,' says Beverley Milne. As a musician gives life to a piano piece, the t'ai-chi expert will sing the form with his own body.

What to expect

T'ai-chi is a personal experience and essentially a solo exercise, yet it is best for a beginner to work in a small group of not more than ten people. The energy generated by working with others builds concentration on the process. Individual guidance is a must – t'ai-chi cannot be learned from a book; although the separate positions can be illustrated, the fluidity of moving from one into another needs demonstration and, initially, a degree of mimicry. Nothing in t'ai-chi is static and thus it ultimately defies written instruction. The teacher teaches with her own body, so watching and being observed are essential.

The sequence is built up gradually, with movements added only when each person is sure of what has gone before. Teachers like Beverley Milne maintain that two years' training is necessary to impart fully the complete form, although others may teach it in less. T'ai-chi looks disarmingly simple, but it is hard to do well. Maintaining its calm pace without haste, its discipline without rigidity, are inner attunements rather than memorized steps. For many people the hardest thing is to learn to let go, to become natural, flowing and unimpeded. Practice helps and for most people this means a weekly class, with some time alone as often as can be managed. Dawn or dusk are said to be good times to perform the t'ai-chi.

Who benefits?

T'ai-chi does different things for each individual, but results may be felt from the very first lesson. Usually it slows down the system, which most people feel as a major benefit. It stabilizes and equalizes the energy flow, reducing the pressure of stress; 'You are less likely to fly off the handle', says Beverley Milne, 'and instead can free-flow with situations.' Other results she mentions are the ability to maintain concentration, and clearer, less distracted thought patterns. Grace, tranquillity and the ability to remain 'centred' are also frequently reported.

Personal view

● *Rachel, 40, personal assistant.* This is my second time around doing t'ai-chi. I started it eight years ago, had a four-year gap when I had a baby and then took it up again a year and a half ago. My teacher goes very slowly; we have got about two-thirds through the long form this time. You have to keep practising what you have done and it takes time to build up. If you're at a tricky stage you need to consolidate, just learning one twist at a time, and to keep going back. It's as if you aren't so much learning as absorbing through your body. Sometimes you almost anticipate the next move, but not always; for instance, the kicking movements don't always seem to follow on naturally.

It is difficult to do properly and sometimes quite hard work physically, although it looks very slow. It's very precise in things like the way you move, the angles, the degree to which you turn your foot – getting these right is very important in order not to strain and to be centred and grounded. But there is a wonderful atmosphere in a class, where everyone is doing it silently and in unison, it's quite magical really. You can get that feeling doing it alone at home if you take time and centre yourself first but it's more difficult, especially when you are constrained for space and have to keep moving to avoid the sofa.

My teacher incorporates the essence and meaning of each movement and how it relates to the ego and the psyche – it can be quite profound. How much of that one absorbs is up to the individual.

I go to classes once a week and very occasionally do some at home. Sometimes I go full of the day's irritabilities but I always feel much calmer at the end of a session. It gives me an hour of peace and tranquillity in my week, and I'm sure I'd gain even more if I did it more often.

Recently I learned to ride a bicycle and after only ten minutes I'd got the hang of it – I maintain that was probably because of the balance which I'd got from t'ai-chi.

Where to go

British T'ai Chi Ch'üan
Association
7 Upper Wimpole Street
London W1
Tel: 01-935-8444

School of T'ai Chi Ch'üan
5 Tavistock Place
London WC1
Tel: 01-459-0764

What is it?

Yoga is one of the oldest methods of uniting, or harmonizing, mind and body. The word *yoga* means unity, from the Sanskrit *yuj*, to bind, join or yoke. Yoga is an ancient Indian philosophy, a total system of thought and action that provides the practitioner with the self-discipline both to deal with everyday life in a balanced fashion and, should one so wish, to develop on a spiritual path leading to liberation of the soul.

Yoga has its origins in prehistory and for thousands of years it was a secret technique carried out by barely accessible coteries. In the nineteenth century civil servants and soldiers returning from service in India and scholars of Indian philosophy began to make yoga known in the West. Since then it has rapidly gained popularity, helped by visits to the West by Indian yogis (yoga practitioners) such as Vivekananda, Vishnu Devananda and B. K. S. Iyengar.

Although to many people yoga conjures up images of bodies twisted into knots and people standing on their heads, the physical activity is but one of a number of yogic paths. It is termed hatha yoga (in Sanskrit *ha* means sun and *tha*, moon, suggesting the uniting of two opposites) and has become the most popular form of yoga in the West, where it is often used as a way to physical fitness. It can be used as a simple exercise routine, although it produces results that other physical exercises seldom bring: profound relaxation and tranquillity of mind.

There are yoga disciplines for all aspects of life. Karma yoga, for example, is the yoga of practical work, which advises the follower to perform tasks for the common good, without anxiety over results or desire for reward. Raja yoga, is the yoga of the mind, dealing with mental reactions and aiming at control over negative conditions such as doubt, anger and fear. Bhakti yoga is for the religious devotee, and development is attained through prayer and worship.

This chapter is about physical, hatha, yoga. Not only does it fit into the bodywork confines of this book, but it is also the most widespread and accessible form of yoga available to us today. It is traditionally considered a step on the ladder of self-development, not an end in itself. Its prerequisite is to master the practical and moral requirements of everyday life: cleanliness, non-violence, truth, sincerity, non-acquisitiveness and self-study. Only after attending to these should detailed attention be given to the physical body.

Hatha yoga is primarily the performance of *asanas* – physical postures – in order to develop a perfectly functioning body, not as an object of pride but so that it can be forgotten. A trouble-free body helps concentration on the spiritual practices of yoga: breath control, which is concerned with the subtle energy flow and vitality of the whole being; and the initial stages of meditation, controlling the mind and concentration. When, as a result of meditation, the thought processes are stilled, the final stage, *samadhi*, is reached. In Indian philosophy this is a state of absolute bliss in which the spirit is no longer bound by the body and personality and can free itself from the cycle of life and death.

Of course, you do not have to pursue the spiritual aspects of yoga. Millions of people have found a simple hatha yoga evening class once a week or doing some of the postures a few times a week at home brings tremendous physical benefits. Yet yoga differs from many other forms of exercise in two major ways.

Firstly, yoga is not competitive. That means there is no

success or failure. Each person does his best, according to the structure and limitations of his own body. Secondly, concentration is far more important than how wide an individual's legs will stretch or how far his back will bend. An acrobat does not necessarily make a good yoga student, for yoga is to do with inward focusing, concentrating on a slow stretch and what it does right down through the fibres of the body from skin to bone.

The postures of yoga

Yoga has hundreds of postures. They range from standing still and lying down to the contorted torso twists, which are impossible unless you practise several hours a day. However, only some twenty or so postures form the basis of most yoga classes, with a range of others introduced according to pupil standard and the training and preferences of the teacher.

Each posture has three stages: going in, holding and coming out. There are no fast, jerky movements. Everything is kept under control. The whole body is involved. Often students may be told to think about their left heel when performing a posture primarily to do with stretching the right arm. They may be reminded of their fingertips or eyeballs, or of what the skin of the armpit or the bone of a hip is doing. Thus the posture becomes an integration, not a mechanical, repetitive performance.

This approach prevents the overuse of more flexible parts of the body, a natural tendency, which yoga postures reveal. Thus, if back bends are easy for someone with hyperflexibility at the base of the spine, the observant teacher will demand that this student checks that low back mobility and concentrates on the middle to upper spine. Suddenly the bendable back is not so limber, but the student will have a new awareness of where his rigidities, and therefore his imbalances, lie.

Correct performance of the hatha yoga postures invokes a kind of body intelligence, a co-ordination of mental and physical activity. Through applying mental energy to the way in which a posture is done, the harmonious action of mind and body is achieved.

The science of yoga

The yoga postures evolved out of intuitive awareness of what was good for the body and, perhaps, from careful observation of the natural world, since many postures are named after animals and birds, such as the cat, the cobra, the dog, the eagle and the crow. Today the postures are the subject of scientific investigation, mainly in the United States and India, verifying what the practitioners of ancient times knew. Swami Rama, an Indian yoga teacher and founder of the Himalaya Institute for Research and Yoga Therapy in America, explains:

In order to unravel and dispel the obstacles that stood in the way of attaining the expanded consciousness and awareness that they sought, the yogic masters were forced over the ages to deal, one by one, with the different aspects of man's functioning. The functions of the body were systematically explored through postures, or *asanas*. Intricacies of respiration and breathing patterns were studied in great detail. The workings of the mind were catalogued and explained.

This careful and precise approach to the functions of mind and body established a series of clearly defined, easily reproducible, and, at the same time, beneficial practices which can profitably be studied in the modern laboratory. The application of techniques for measuring physiological processes to the study of yoga and statistical analysis of the results has brought together a picture of an impressive wealth of therapeutic techniques.

Documented evidence shows that the postures, together with breathing exercises, can effectively improve muscular efficiency, reduce the incidence of asthma attacks, increase red blood cell count, lower heart rate, manage hypertension and aid parasympathetic nervous system function.

Yoga is increasingly being used therapeutically on its own and as an adjunct to osteopathy, chiropractic and orthodox medical treatment.

What to expect

Although some people may be attracted to yoga by a book and try to do the postures alone at home, a teacher is essential in the beginning to make sure you are getting things right. It is all too easy to think you are doing what the book says, whereas in reality your body is behaving very differently. Ideally the yoga class should be supplemented by practice at home. Many people go to one or two classes a week, and do a short home practice of, say, 15 to 30 minutes each day.

Classes vary a great deal and it is very important to pick a well-trained and, preferably, personally recommended teacher whom you feel is sympathetic and whose classes give you a perceptible sense of change. You should be able to ask questions and feel keenly observed without criticism. A good teacher will manage to keep an eye on, and give some personal attention to, everyone. Traditionally yoga was taught one-to-one, master to student, an ideal method for ensuring the basics are correctly learned.

What kind of class should you attend? There are several schools of yoga, so do make sure the teacher has been trained by one of them. Probably most popular in Britain is the British Wheel of Yoga, which offers a thorough grounding in practice and theory. Also well respected is the Yoga for Health Foundation training, which like the Wheel of Yoga offers a good, middle-of-the road basis.

The Sivananda and Iyengar trainings are more traditional. Sivananda classes go through a routine of twelve postures with some breathing exercises. The routine is fairly strenuous but has the advantage that once learned it can be done at home and offers the opportunity of becoming proficient in a limited number of postures. The system was devised by Swami Vishnu Devananda, a disciple of Swami Sivananda, who did much to popularize yoga in America and Europe.

The system devised by B. K. S. Iyengar provides very solid and precise training in physical yoga. Based on the traditional postures, with his own variations added, Iyengar's system specializes in strengthening and disciplining the body. Some of its postures are very advanced. Strong and challenging, it appeals to the more dedicated practitioner, although it is carefully graded to include beginners too.

A yoga class can last from one to two and a half hours. The atmosphere is quiet and harmonious and students are often asked to lie down and rest before starting. This enables the body to gather its forces and the mind to drop its activity so that one can concentrate on the session. Some classes have a simple warming up routine as with aerobic exercise, for it is advisable to stretch and prepare for any form of physical action.

The class will be divided into standing, seated and/or lying postures. You seldom go straight from one posture into another; there usually is a rest and recovery period of a few seconds between them. Each pose is also followed by a counter-pose; thus backbends are followed by forward bends, and stretches to the left are followed by stretches to the right. Many of the postures are concerned with holding the balance, the headstand being one of the more advanced.

At no time should there be any strain; the movement is geared to a long, slow stretch, locking that stretched position for some seconds and then relaxing. Each person works to his own capacity. The person with stiff hamstrings will get as much from a forward bend as someone who flops with ease.

Standing still and lying down are also yoga postures in their own right. In a class you will learn how to stand so the body is evenly balanced without tension, and how to lie in a way most conducive to complete, inner relaxation (the corpse pose).

Breathing exercises may start or complete the class, and instruction on how to breathe with each posture is common too. The breathing is aimed at harmonizing in- and out-breath and is timed or counted with retentions, according to the exercise. As with the physical postures, the intention is to gain control.

Meditation practices may be included in some classes. These can take the form of chanting (to concentrate on a word or sound), gazing at a candle flame or concentrating on the breath, all designed to help you become focused and to filter out extraneous thought.

Classes end with a long relaxation period, often guided by the teacher, who may give verbal instructions for progressively dropping tension from each part of the body. After a class you will feel rather like an evenly stretched elastic band. There may be some small ache in areas of the body unused to movement, but generally it will be a 'good' ache and encourage further activity. Commonly, students become more in touch with their bodies, with an accompanying heightened perception of what is going on round them. They report the balancing effects of a class: start off tired, and a sense of rejuvenation results; come in overstimulated, and a class will calm and pleasantly slow

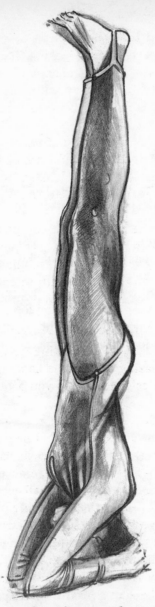

The headstand is one of yoga's more advanced postures; there are several others that also teach balance and tranquillity.

you down. This balancing act, so important in an age of conflicting demands, is one of yoga's chief advantages.

Who benefits?

It is impossible to designate anyone a yoga 'type'; practitioners are all shapes and sizes, and from all walks of life. The one common factor is the desire to improve health and awareness. Often people are drawn to yoga by the desire to combat tension or sickness, having heard, for example, how it helped a neighbour's arthritis or eased a friend's nervous troubles. It can be used by the disabled to improve mobility and by the able-bodied to increase achievement. Some people are attracted by yoga's self-discipline, for help in, say, giving up smoking or controlling food intake. It is also for the person who wants to keep fit – with bonuses. Ultimately it can promote a kind of spiritual serenity beyond the bounds of any other physical exercise.

Personal view

● *Sarah, 40, historian.* I started practising yoga fifteen
  years ago. I thought it might help me relax – I have
  quite a nervous temperament and used to get easily
  agitated. The first thing I noticed was that I was so
  much slower after a class. For me that was excellent,
  as it actually helped my concentration and made me
  more efficient, instead of all anxious and dithery.
  Another result was that it seemed to open out my
  senses. If I sat down to a meal after a class, I was
  tasting things as if for the first time. That made me
  more aware of what I really wanted to eat and when,

and my weight began to even out – I had been an obsessive dieter previously.

The physical exercise made my whole body shape change within a couple of years. From looking insubstantial, I had more presence and stability, in all ways, and other people began to remark on it.

I found I could cope better with the everyday ups and downs of life. Whenever I went on long journeys, for instance, I used to end up terribly exhausted, but by doing some yoga before and afterwards I can now dispel that tiredness and just get on with what I have to do without worrying. I'm no longer so prone to coughs and colds, yet when I do get ill, it is a short, sharp sickness, then over fast. My physical healing abilities seem to have improved as has my general mental coping mechanism. I feel more detached somehow from the things that used to cause instant negative reactions. Altogether I feel more in charge of my life.

Where to go

British Wheel of Yoga
31 Mercian Court
Park Place
Cheltenham,
Gloucestershire
Tel: 0242-581336

Iyengar Yoga Institute
223a Randolph Avenue
London W9 INL
Tel: 01-624 3080

Sivananda Yoga Centre
50 Chepstow Villas
London W11
Tel: 01-229-7970

Yoga for Health
Foundation
Ickwell Bury
Northill
Biggleswade, Bedfordshire
SG18 9EF
Tel: 076-727-271/604

OTHER

THERAPIES

The importance of the therapies in this section is no less than that of those treated at greater length; they are given less coverage because of their unavailability. Practitioner training in all of them is given only abroad and any therapists in this country tend to be itinerant or lone.

Aston-Patterning

The aim of Aston work is to help people identify their own stress-induced movement habits, and then to use the body 'intelligence' to find more comfortable and effective ways of behaving. The teacher will observe the client's movement, seeing where he braces or holds himself, where he is restricted and where he is protecting himself. She may also look for scientific clues, such as proportion of vertical to lateral movement in the tissues, and for 'co-operative movement', to determine which parts of the body interact harmoniously and which seem to fight against one another. She may note the timing or speed of action, and where in the body certain movements start; many people thrust their hips forward before the rest of the body moves, or stick out the head prior to moving the legs, for instance. Thus the body is viewed as an overall system.

Judith Aston, who started the method after working in dance and choreography and with Ida Rolf (see p. 149), noticed two major factors in dealing with bodies: people are asymmetrical and all movement occurs in spirals.

To put right imbalances such as those above, she determined that people must take account of these factors as they relearn how to move.

There are three components to Aston-Patterning after the initial observation. First is movement education. The teacher uses gentle techniques to loosen overworked areas: simple cues as the student performs movements result in increased awareness.

Massage, the second focus, works on tissue and joints to help them release unnecessary tension. It is followed by environmental tailoring. Objects in daily use, like chairs, car seats, desks, tools, even shoes, are usually designed for some theoretically 'average' body. The person not fitting that design is in trouble. Through constantly trying to adapt to the shape of these objects, we create new tensions and rigidities. Once aware of these stresses, the offending objects can be altered according to one's individual proportions and patterns. To this end, a session may take place at home or work.

Sessions are arranged between teacher and client, and will be different in combination and number according to the individual's needs. Four to six sessions, each lasting from one to two hours, are usually recommended. Those who may benefit from Aston-Patterning include children, pregnant women, the disabled, cyclists, runners and other athletes, anyone wishing to relieve chronic muscle stress or simply to move with more grace.

Eutony

'Eutony', says its originator Gerda Alexander, 'is a Western way of experiencing the unity of the total person.' The word derives from the Greek prefix *eu*, meaning well or harmonious, and *tonus*, or tension. While rooted in the body, eutony takes practitioners further, into a deep-felt awareness of their being and how it relates to the world around it.

Gerda Alexander was born in Germany in 1908, and was involved in dance, especially the experimental new movement of the 1920s and 1930s. She sought, however, to develop further, for although pupils were learning so-called 'free movement', they were really taught to copy their teachers. She recognized a need to teach not by imitation, but by allowing pupils to learn for themselves through experiencing their own bodies. Her own health problems (she suffered from heart disease when young) also directed her interest towards ways of maintaining fitness.

One image gives insight into her work: the juggler who can roll or stop a ball at any point along the forearm. It is a trick no one can teach; the individual has to gain control of his own muscles and learn sensitivity before succeeding. It is this kind of aware sensitivity that Gerda Alexander explored and communicated. Teacher Therese Melville Van Cauwenberghe, a Belgian who teaches eutony in London, explains:

Through subtle observation you will learn to know
yourself by feeling what is happening in yourself, from
the outer boundary of your skin to the inner space of
your bones, joints and vital organs. You will develop
your sense of touch, awaken your whole sensitivity.
You will learn to become aware of and release tensions
which may have cramped your movements, impeded
your circulation and breathing, disturbed your
digestion and posture.
Tensions diminish our sensitivity and capacity to
respond both emotionally and physically. Eutony aims
to achieve a better-balanced distribution of tonus
through the body and to restore its adaptability. It is

the desire for wakefulness, for increased sensitivity,
that is at its core.

In the process of self-discovery eutony can reveal inner
weaknesses, yet at the same time discover hidden resources.
It is a long, gradual process towards harmony, both in the
physical structure and the inner, emotional being. 'Developing awareness and sensitivity is an integral part of the progression towards maturity; it takes time,' says Therese.

During their four-year training eutonists work deeply on
their own inner balance before teaching others. Tuition
takes place either in groups or individually.

The one-to-one approach is more intimate than a group
session, and includes hands-on work: the eutonist 'listens'
with her hands. Central to eutony is always respect for the
student. Gerda Alexander spoke about personal sessions
thus: 'When you help the other person by your own will,
you invade him and usually make him even more tense. It
is very important to begin all treatment with this in mind:
what does the other body need?'

No two lessons are the same. The instructions vary and
the personal experience changes every time; eutony is never
passive, mechanical repetition. The tutor proposes lines to
explore, leaving the class to develop as the exploration proceeds. In so doing, said Gerda Alexander, the student is
helped 'to stand on his own two feet, to liberate himself to
find his own security'.

Descriptions of the work in action may be misrepresentative, because the intention is to get beyond predetermined movement. Like several other disciplines, eutony
causes dramatic insight into what one is doing within the
body, particularly in creating stressed function. Unlike the
others, though, it steers clear of imposing alternative action;
it works primarily by self-knowledge.

A number of things may happen. Starting lying down,

you might be asked to feel into your hands, from the bones outwards, appreciating any differences in sensitivity between each finger, the number of bones and where the joints are. Then you might be given a stick of bamboo, asked to handle it and be aware of all the sensations it provides, then to experience the increased sensitivity of that side of the body.

Another time you could be asked to touch the floor with every area of the skin surface; this causes you to stretch and move in previously undreamed-of ways. You could then be asked to push yourself away from a resisting surface, like a floor or wall, using the strength of your bone structure. While none of these may necessarily happen, explorations on similar lines, inspired by each class, help you to find out what your body does and to express yourself physically in new ways. Pain may emerge, denoting a new awareness of unknown tensions; increased sensitivity may not necessarily be comfortable.

Therese Melville Van Cauwenberghe likes to present her classes with a skeleton, so they can see, for instance, precisely how the hip joint is shaped or exactly where the thigh bone joins the pelvis. 'Most people are unaware of this,' she believes, and an incorrect body image makes people misuse the structure. Seeing how the skeleton is constructed, students can, instead of ignoring it, integrate and trust it, gaining a new sense of inner security in many ways.

Eutony has a strong psychotherapeutic aspect and has been used in conjunction with analytical therapy. Its attention to movement can take students back to non-verbal experience and the primitive sense of touch with an intense freshness like that of a baby, and it can help new dreams and memories to emerge. Ultimately, Gerda Alexander discovered, eutony could stimulate artistic understanding and increase spiritual perception. By deepening the whole range of experience, she believed, we can become conscious of the body as manifesting spiritual creation.

Rosen method

Rosen is an extremely gentle approach to physical and emotional awareness through relaxation. Marion Rosen, originator of the method, was born in Germany, where she studied breathing and relaxation methods and their connection to psychotherapy in the 1930s. Later she went to Stockholm, where she became a licensed physiotherapist, and emigrated to the United States in 1940. She now trains therapists in California and in Sweden.

While giving patients physiotherapy Marion Rosen noticed that there was a connection between relaxation and physical comfort: when people relaxed, their pains disappeared. She also observed that as musculature began to soften, people would open up and entrust her with important details about their lives, often things they had long held secret. Now she is convinced that people who confide in others have greater immunity to disease.

Rosen became interested in how and why relaxation occurred, seeking answers to questions such as, 'What is necessary for people to relax?' She developed ways of touching to enable relaxation to happen, with light massage-type movements but placing the hands in a much firmer way wherever she felt areas of holding. She explains, 'When people are tense, they start by feeling they have to hold something in, they pull themselves into a smaller space, then the muscles hold and form a coat of armour. Then these become places where the muscles have forgotten how to work. When you touch that area, the hand doesn't go in, it is not received. Then we wait and see what the person will do as they are holding. It is a form of listening with the hands, feeling for all the signals, asking, why would that little jump come just then?'

The therapist lets the body give its own answers about what is going on. 'It never lies,' says Marion Rosen. Sometimes she gets mental images that give clues, and often sees the age when a particular trauma occurred stored in body and face. 'The body is a total mirror of every thought and emotion that we have.' Gently the client is informed of what the therapist senses, and than a kind of surrender can occur. One patient says,

I was disappointed at first when nothing much at all seemed to be going on. After about fifteen or twenty minutes, I was asked to turn over onto my stomach, and at that point I must have relaxed and given up all my expectations because the next thirty minutes were a new experience. I had many different feelings, including a lot of anger. At one point I seemed to experience being born. I drifted through a series of experiences which came and went, and I felt each one, but did not hang on to it. I was aware that my breathing was changing all the time – at one point it almost stopped altogether – and felt just as one does when in a hypnotic trance.

Another reports, 'It was very restful, peaceful, harmonious. The treatment was virtually imperceptible, it was gentle and deep. It felt like cutting through a fog.' Someone else, who received the therapy standing up on a train, said 'I felt my brain calming down.'

Rosen work concentrates a lot on breathing patterns, and particularly the movement of the diaphragm as breath comes and goes. 'The breath is an indicator, a monitor,' says Marion Rosen, 'and the diaphragm is very sensitive. It forms a wall when we want to protect ourselves. When it moves fully, our physical well-being is that much greater.

We are in a state of good health when the diaphragm swings, and we can enjoy peace and fulfilment. The aim of the work is to have the breath restored to the body, so the body works like it is meant to. When we hold tight, the breathing doesn't go to the diaphragm, it is not alive.'

Rosen work is highly intuitive; it is done with much wisdom, understanding and, above all, empathy. Undoubtedly, it can make real, positive long-term changes, often after just one session. 'When the part of the body we work on has relaxed, the problem seems to resolve itself. It no longer has the same impact, it is like the veil being taken off.' Often what happens is beyond emotional release: 'Crying can be above emotions, sometimes more happens with one tear that comes from a great depth. Once you come to a place of acceptance of who you are, there is a possibility to meet life in a different way.'

As one client said after a treatment, 'I rediscovered my heart and my enthusiasm for life, threw off my feelings of being deceived.'

Trager

Milton Trager is an American doctor and an original and intuitive therapist who formulated a way of influencing the patient's fundamental feelings through the use of hand pressure. Central to his approach is something Milton Trager calls 'hook-up', best described as a state of active meditation in which the therapist's relaxed, alert, very sensitive state connects deeply with the patient in a totally unforced, undemanding way.

Technique of any kind is nonexistent in Trager work; 'I hook up, and I go,' he says. The aim is to impart to the patient the sense of what an integrated mind and body feels like. 'This is transmitted through the autonomic nervous system from the therapist's mind, though his hands, to the involved area. The feeling is picked up in the patient's mind because of the manner in which the tissues are worked, creating the feeling of real relaxation,' Trager explains.

No physical condition is without its psychological counterpart, Trager believes. The mind projects its patterns into the body tissues, and they are imprinted because of outside circumstances: accidents, surgery, posture, daily stress and so on. Our patterns of physical tension, then, are mostly in the mind. Therefore, instead of trying to change them at tissue level, Trager influences the unconscious, feeling state.

Once traumas have been recorded on body tissue, Trager believes, they cannot be erased. It is possible, however, to induce new, positive feelings that influence the mind and body for the better. The patient can learn how to feel integrated and co-ordinated, and connected to the surrounding 'force which sustains everything', as he puts it. Our usual state is to be so blocked and tense that this force cannot enter our consciousness; once it is allowed past the self-erected barriers, we alter deeply.

In a session lasting about one hour the therapist uses very light, steady, rhythmic movements. If he finds areas of stiffness or hardening, unlike many other manipulative therapists, the Trager practitioner does not impose greater pressure. Instead he will become lighter and more sensitive in order to create a sensation of freedom and ease. Thus the patient's mind is taken away from pain and contraction, and turned instead to consider what freedom and lightness would feel like.

The practitioner is not the sole bestower of healing. At a certain point during every treatment the power transfers to the patient. Describing one such incident, Trager says, 'There was a transmission from my mind, through my hands to the patient's tissues, and then to his mind. At that moment, unbeknownst to him, he became the therapist and sent the message to his tissues. I felt this nutritive change in my hands. His tissues were then able to receive stimuli from the central nervous system.'

After treatment come 'mentastics' (Trager's amalgamation of 'mental gymnastics'), in which patients are taught how to maintain and re-create mentally the healthy, positive feeling occurring when the tissue was in the practitioner's hands.

Trager has worked on patients with severe problems, including multiple sclerosis, muscular dystrophy and disablement due to oxygen deprivation at birth, producing great improvements. Medical tests on the muscular dystrophy patient showed 12 out of 18 muscles strengthened, 10–20 per cent increase in hearing ability and, perhaps most important, he reported, 'My belief system was changed in the direction of a positive expectancy of health and muscle strength away from the negative expectation of progressive muscle weakness.' Trager work can help the most common disorders equally successfully.

Trager's approach is subtle, relying on the state of the practitioner and what he is able to transmit to the patient. It is not, however, mystical or esoteric. Explains Trager therapist Deane Juhan, 'The kind of reflex responses, tissue changes and behavioural changes he is able to elicit are possible because of the intimate neurological associations between sensory stimulation, emotional feelings, attitudes and concepts, and the body's motor response to all of them. The fact that they profoundly influence one another is abundantly clear. And it is equally clear that the unconscious forces which control their relationships may be turned from a vicious circle into a fruitful one.'

Where to go

Aston-Patterning

Institute of Structural
Bodywork
8 Cervantes Court
Ruston Mews
London W11 1UE
Tel: 01-243-0132

Eutony

Therese Melville Van
Cauwenberghe
68 Huntingdon Street
London N1
Tel: 01-607-5248

International Association
of Gerda Alexander
Eutony (AIEGA)
69 Rue du Rhone
1207 Geneva, Switzerland
Tel: 022-35-34-70

Rosen method

Anita Saunders
55 Cranford Park Drive
Yateley, Surrey GU17 7LB
Tel: 0252-877351

Lena Austin
Director of Studies
Axelsons Gymnastika
Institut
Gastrikegatan 10
S-113 24 Stockholm,
Sweden
Tel: 010-468-165360

Trager

Institute of Structural
Bodywork
8 Cervantes Court
Ruston Mews
London W11 1UE
Tel: 01-243-0132

The Trager Institute
300 Poplar Avenue
Suite 5
Mill Valley
California 94941
USA

FURTHER READING

General

David Boadella, *Lifestreams*, London, Routledge & Kegan Paul, 1987
————*Wilhelm Reich*, London, Arkana, 1985
Christopher Connolly and Hetty Einzig, *The Fitness Jungle*, London, Century Hutchinson, 1986
Nevill Drury, *The Bodywork Book*, Australia, Prism Alpha, 1984
Richard Strozzi Heckler, *The Anatomy of Change*, Boulder, Colorado, Shambala, 1984
Ron Kurtz and Hector Prestera, *The Body Reveals*, New York, Harper & Row, 1984

Aerobic exercise

Kenneth Cooper MD, *Aerobics Programme for Total Well-Being*, London, Bantam, 1985

Aikido

Koichi Tohei, *Aikido*, London, Souvenir Press, 1975
A. Westbrook and O. Ratti, *Aikido and the Dynamic Sphere*, Rutland Vermont, Charles E. Tuttle, 1984

Alexander Technique

Wilfred Barlow, *The Alexander Principle*, London, Arrow Books, 1983
Edward Maisel (ed), *The Alexander Technique*, London, Thames and Hudson, 1974

Aromatherapy

Shirley Price, *Practical Aromatherapy*, Wellingborough, Thorsons, 1983

Robert Tisserand, *Aromatherapy for Everyone*, London, Penguin Books, 1988

Biodynamics

Gerda Boyesen and Mona Lisa Boyesen, *Biodynamic Theory of Neurosis*, London, Biodynamic Psychology Publications, 1980

Bioenergetics

Alexander Lowen, *Bioenergetics*, London, Penguin Books, 1978

Dancercise

Phyllis Greene Morgan, *Dancercise*, London, Methuen, 1983

Dance therapy

Elaine and David Feder, *The Expressive Arts Therapies*, Englewood Cliffs, New Jersey, Prentice-Hall, 1981

Eutony

Gerda Alexander, *Eutony*, New York, Felix Morrow, 1985

Feldenkrais method

Moshe Feldenkrais, *Awareness through Movement*, London, Penguin Books, 1987

Hellerwork

Joseph Heller and William A. Henkin, *Bodywise*, Los Angeles, Jeremy P. Tarcher, 1986

Massage

Gordon Inkeles, *The New Massage*, London, George Allen & Unwin, 1980

Dolores Krieger, *The Therapeutic Touch*, New Jersey, Prentice-Hall, Englewood Cliffs, 1979

Lucinda Lidell and others, *The Book of Massage*, London, Ebury Press, 1984

Frances M. Tappan, *Healing Massage Techniques*, Virginia, Reston Publishing Company, 1980

Neuro-muscular technique

Leon Chaitow, *Soft-Tissue Manipulation*, Wellingborough, Thorsons, 1987

Polarity therapy

Alan Siegel, *Polarity Therapy*, Bridport, Prism Press, 1987

Postural Integration

Jack Painter, *Deep Bodywork and Personal Development*, USA, Bodymind Books, 1987

Reflexology

Dwight C. Byers, *Better Health with Foot Reflexology*, Florida, Ingham Publishing, 1983

Relaxation

James Hewitt, *Relaxation East and West*, London, Rider, 1982

Kenneth R. Pelletier, *Mind as Healer, Mind as Slayer*, London, George Allen & Unwin, 1977

William Johnston, *Silent Music*, Glasgow, Collins, 1974

Rolfing

R. Feitis (ed), *Ida Rolf Talks about Rolfing and Physical Reality*, Boulder, Colorado, Rolf Institute, 1978

Ida P. Rolf, *Rolfing: The Integration of Human Structures*, Santa Monica, California, Dennis-Landman, 1977

Shiatsu

Carola Beresford-Cooke, *Massage for Healing and Relaxation*, London, Arlington Books, 1986

Wataru Ohashi, *Do-It-Yourself Shiatsu*, London, George Allen & Unwin, 1979

T'ai-chi

Al Chung-liang Huang, *Embrace Tiger, Return to Mountain*, New York, Bantam, 1978

Yoga

James Funderburk, *Science Studies Yoga*, U S A, Himalayan International Institute, 1977

James Hewitt, *Yoga Postures*, London, Barrie & Jenkins, 1977

Cheryl Isaacson, *Yoga for all Ages*, Wellingborough, Thorsons, 1986

B. K. S. Iyengar, *Light on Yoga*, London, George Allen & Unwin, 1976.

INDEX

abdomen, 104, 111, 152
accidents, 24, 19
acupuncture, 100, 108, 121, 124
adrenalin, 133
Africa, 83
ageing process, 20, 154
aikido, 15, 18, 33–42
alcohol, 138
alertness, 110
Alexander, F. Matthias, 43–7,
    48; Gerda, 188, 190;
    Technique, 16, 18, 43–53
alignment, 146, 171
alimentary canal, 54, 55
amenorrhoea, 136
America, 76, 98
anatomy, 101
anger, 63, 64, 75, 152, 160, 162
ankles, 68
antidepressants, 21
anxiety, 60, 75, 134, 137
Arabia, 83
arm, unbendable, 36
armouring, 13
arms, 64, 82, 139, 146, 151
arthritis, 60, 99, 136
asanas, 177, 179; see also
    yoga
asthma, 100, 136, 180
Aston, Judith, 186
athletes, 136, 187
attention, 44
Awareness through Movement,
    92
awareness, 44, 93, 188, 191
Ayurvedic medicine, 124

babies, 63
back, 47, 64, 68, 69, 104, 110,

117, 152; backache, 55, 60,
    117; bad, 128; pain, 24
balance, 108, 110, 150, 151, 158,
    162, 171, 182
baldness, 106
behind, 153
Benson, Dr Herbert, 135
bioenergetics, 63–74, 159
bioenergy, 56
biofeedback, 138, 140
birth, 152
blood, 16, 27, 56, 99; flow, 26,
    99; pressure, 20, 134, 135, 136;
    see also circulation, red blood
    cells, white blood cells
Boadella, David, 14, 16
body, building, 112; conditioning,
    29; language, 12, 170
bodywork, 16, 122, 125, 126,
    157, 158
bone, 16, 58, 99, 148, 178, 188,
    190; fracture, 99; structure, 88
bow exercise, 67
bowel, 133
Boyesen, Gerda, 55–7
brain, 27, 44, 45, 92, 100
brainwaves, 99, 134, 140, 141
breath, 15, 120, 159, 160, 162,
    172, 177
breathing, 36, 64, 65, 66, 78, 88,
    93, 111, 133, 139, 140, 142,
    146, 151, 154, 179, 180, 188,
    192, 193
British Wheel of Yoga, 180
Burns, Harvey, 147, 154, 155

cancer, 136, 138
Carruthers, Dr Malcolm, 135,
    136, 138, 139

catharsis, 79, 89, 155
cerebro-spinal fluid, 56
Chace, Marian, 76
Chaitow, Boris, 107; Leon, 107
Chang San-feng, 169
check-up, medical, 23
chest, 14, 146, 151, 158, 160
chi, 120, 167; *see also ki*, life
   force, *prana*
childbirth, 140
children, 39, 63, 79, 87, 128,
   187
China, 98, 120, 124, 167
chiropractic, 123, 126
chiropractors, 101
choice, 44
cigarettes, 138
circuit training, 27
circulation, 20, 26, 99, 134, 188;
   see also blood
colds, 21
colitis, 136
communication, 78, 98, 162
concentration, 36, 115, 167
conception, 152
confidence, 22, 37, 81, 89
connective tissue, 16, 146, 148,
   150, 160; *see also* fascia, tissue
Connolly, Christopher, 92, 93,
   95
consciousness, 43, 45, 121, 125,
   137
constipation, 136
Cooper, Dr Kenneth, 20
coordination, 16, 37, 44
counselling, 122, 125
creativity, 64, 83
criticism, 88
cycling, 19, 27
cyclists, 187
Cyriax, Dr James, 101

dance, 18, 29, 75–86, 167, 188
dancers, 117
degenerative disease, 21, 57

depression, 21, 60, 134, 136
dermatitis, 136
detoxification, 124
diagnosis, 107
diaphragm, 14, 192, 193
diarrhoea, 56, 60, 136
diet, 122, 124, 125; *see also*
   nutrition
digestion, 26, 88, 188
digestive, disorders, 128;
   process, 54
disablement, 187, 195
disease, 120, 122
distress, 70
dizziness, 126
doctors, 111
dojo, 35
drinking, 26
drugs, 105, 127, 138

eating, 26
ECG, 23, 99
ecstasy, 75
eczema, 136
education, 88
effleurage, 102
elbow, 108, 146, 157
elements, 122, 123
elimination, 88
emotional, problems, 128;
   reactions, 60; release, 56
emotions, 55, 63, 64, 70, 81, 89,
   147, 152, 155, 158, 170, 193
empathy, 193
end-gaining, 45
endorphins, 20, 99
energy, 20, 54, 56, 64, 65, 66,
   67, 75, 78, 120, 121, 122, 123,
   125, 126, 149, 154, 160, 162,
   173, 177
enlightenment, 142
enuresis, 136
Esalen Institute, 91
Espenak, Liljan, 77
essential oils, 106

evolution, 48

exercise, 12, 19–32, 79, 101, 105, 110, 115, 116, 176, 177; dangers of , 22; pre- check-ups, 23

exhaustion, 43

eyes, 93

face, 14, 152

fascia, 107, 148, 151, 152, 155, 156, 157; *see also* connective tissue, tissue

fat, 20, 116

fear, 17, 37, 56, 70, 75, 162

feet, 47, 67, 82, 108, 120, 151, 171, 189

Feldenkrais, Method, 18, 87–97; Moshe, 88, 89–91

fight, or flight, 134

fingers, 146

flexibility, 156

flu, 21, 56

Fonda, Jane, 28

Fowler, Eileen, 28

Freud, Sigmund, 12, 56, 77

friction, 102

Functional Integration, 92

gastro-intestinal function, 134

Geddes, Gerda, 171

Gestalt, 77

Gladstone, Guy, 72

gravity, 93, 126, 146, 147

Greek civilization, 98

gymnastics, 19

habits, 44, 79, 92

Halprin, Anna, 83

hamstrings, 182

hands, 82, 101, 107, 120, 121, 190

happiness, 75

harmony, 33, 75, 79, 106, 171, 186, 189, 192

hay fever, 136

head, 16, 43, 46, 47, 64, 66, 82, 120, 126, 146, 152, 153, 186; headache, 60

healing, 121

heart, 19, 20, 22, 24, 26, 29, 133, 134, 135, 140, 158, 180; attack, 24, 136

Heckler, Richard, 124

Heller, Joseph, 156, 157, 158

Hellerwork, 18, 156–8

Herdman, Alan, 112, 115, 116, 117, 119

Hewitt, James, 136

Hippocrates, 98

hips, 95, 151, 186

hormonal system, 20

hospitals, 98

human potential movement, 46

humanistic psychology, 14

hypertension, 60, 136, 180

hyperthyroiditis, 136

hypnosis, 138, 141

illness, 24, 82, 99, 120, 170

immunity, 191

India, 98, 120, 124, 161, 176

indigestion, 136

infertility, 140

injuries, 15, 24, 26, 40, 95, 98, 105, 117, 147, 148, 156

Inkeles, Gordon, 100

insomnia, 136

inspiration, 158

integrity, 162

interstitial fluid, 56

intestines, 26, 54, 58

intuition, 106

irritability, 21, 136

Iyengar, B.K.S., 176, 181

Japan, 35, 120

jaw, 14, 93, 152

jogging, 19

joints, 24, 105, 124, 126, 127, 187, 188

judo, 35, 90
Juhan, Deane, 195
Jung, Carl, 77

karate, 35
ki, 33, 37, 39, 120; *see also chi*,
   life force, *prana*
kidney disease, 136
knees, 47, 108, 117, 152
knuckles, 146, 157
Kreiger, Professor Dolores, 98
kung fu, 35
Kurtz, Ron, 14

Laban, Rudolph, 76, 77, 112
lactic acid, 20, 27, 105
laughter, 160
legs, 36, 44, 67, 68, 82, 104,
   113, 114, 137, 146, 151, 152,
   186
Leonard, George, 39
lethargy, 22
Levete, Gina, 77
libido, 56
Lief, Stanley, 107
life force, 15, 33, 57, 108, 120,
   122, 167; *see also chi, ki,*
   prana
ligaments, 26, 99
Ling, Per Henrik, 100
liver, 20, 138
Lowen, Alexander, 65–70
low-impact aerobics, 29
lungs, 19, 20, 22, 29
Luthe, Wolfgang, 138
lymph, 16, 56, 99

manipulation, 107, 124, 126, 146
mantra, 142
martial arts, 33, 34, 35, 36, 89,
   90, 167, 168, 169
massage, 15, 18, 54, 55, 56, 58,
   59, 60, 98–109, 161, 187, 191
meditation, 35, 36, 138, 141,
   142, 161, 167, 177, 182, 193

Melville Van Cauwenberghe,
   Therese, 188, 190
mental, growth, 33; handicap,
   79, 81
mentastics, 195
meridians, 107, 121
metabolism, 105
migraine, 136
Milne, Beverley, 169, 170
mind, 17, 36, 47, 63, 120, 142;
   see also unconscious
Molloy, Mary, 55, 58
monasteries, 169
monks, 33, 169
mood swings, 136
Morgan, Phyllis Greene, 81
mouth, 152
movement, 16, 37, 49, 65, 75,
   78, 79, 81, 82, 83, 87, 92, 110,
   124, 154, 167, 171, 186, 188;
   education, 187
multiple sclerosis, 195
muscles, 14, 16, 19, 20, 22, 26,
   27, 29, 36, 44, 45, 58, 69, 98,
   99, 100, 102, 105, 107, 110,
   113, 114, 115, 116, 125, 133,
   134, 140, 142, 148, 162, 180,
   191
muscular, dystrophy, 195; pain,
   60; spasm, 136; system, 49
musculo-skeletal system,
   93
music, 78, 79, 82
musicians, 49, 95
mystical path, 137

napropathy, 123
naturopathy, 123
nausea, 60, 126
neck, 16, 46, 93, 95, 100, 104,
   110, 151, 153
nervous system, 20, 57, 58, 87,
   93, 100, 134, 135, 154, 180,
   193, 195
nutrition, 28, 122; *see also* diet

organs, 20, 106, 108, 188
orgone energy, 56
osteopaths, 101, 111
osteopathy, 123, 149
oxygen, 19, 20, 151

pain, 60, 64, 85, 90, 95, 104, 105, 107, 108, 136, 150, 156, 190
Painter, Jack, 159
Pare, Ambroise, 101
Parker, Gay, 79
Pelletier, Kenneth, 133, 136
pelvic clock exercise, 93
pelvis, 68, 126, 146, 152
perception, sensory, 43
peristalsis, 54
personal growth, 156
personality, 88
petrissage, 102
philosophy, Chinese, 168, 169; Indian, 176, 177
physical handicap, 95
physiology, 101
physiotherapists, 111
Pilates, Joseph, 111–12; method, 15, 18, 110–19
pleasure, 63, 81
Polarity Therapy, 15, 120–31
posture, 43, 78, 110, 112, 115, 117, 156, 188, 194
prana, 120; *see also chi, ki*, life force
pregnancy, 28, 187
psychiatric patients, 105
psychology, 56, 170
psychotherapy, 55, 57, 140, 147, 190
pulse test, 24

Rajneesh, Bhagwan Shree, 161
randori, 38
recovery rate, 26
red blood cells, 180
reflex points, 100, 104, 107
reflexology, 107, 124

Reich, Wilhelm, 12, 13, 15, 56, 66, 70
relaxation, 13, 18, 37, 39, 43, 58, 104, 107, 132–45, 154, 162, 171, 176, 182, 191, 194
release, 81
repression, 65, 66
respiration, 179
respiratory malfunction, 136
restrictions, 43
rhythm, 75, 81, 82, 150
ribcage, 146, 151
rigidity, 72, 75, 135
ritual, 75
Rolf, Ida, 146, 148, 149, 151, 159, 186
Rolfing, 16, 18, 156–66
Roman civilization, 98
Rosen, Marion, 191
runners, 187
running, 19, 27

sacrum, 126
sadness, 14, 152
samadhi, 177
samurai warriors, 35
Schoop, Trudi, 77
Schultz, Johannes, 138
self-actualization, 137
self-consciousness, 71
self-exposure, 88
self-expression, 65, 70, 78, 81, 158
Selye, Hans, 139
sensitivity, 121, 188, 189, 190
serenity, 184
sexuality, 64, 65, 67
shamans, 75
shape, 116
short-sightedness, 100
shoulders, 44, 55, 63, 95, 100, 104, 105, 111, 126, 146, 151, 153
Sieker, Neerjo, 161, 162
singers, 49

sinusitis, 100
Sivananda, yoga system, 181
skeleton, 190
skiing, 117
skin, 16, 58, 99, 105, 178, 188, 190
skipping, 19
sleep, 134, 141
sleeping pills, 138
sorrow, 162
spine, 100, 102, 124, 126, 146, 151, 153, 160, 171, 178
spirit, 124, 170, 177
spiritual, growth, 33, 137, 167; quest, 172, 177
sports, 105; people, 95, 136, 156
spots, 136
sprains, 26, 105
sprinting, 19
squash, 19
Steiner, Rudolph, 82
stiffness, 27
stomach, 14, 26, 60, 110, 114, 133, 140
Stone, Randolph, 120, 123
stress, 22, 43, 49, 54, 75, 88, 93, 132–3, 135, 136, 138, 139, 143, 156–7, 173, 194; see also tension
stretching, 26, 178, 182
stroke, 95, 136
Structural Integration, 146
surgery, 194
surrender, 170, 192
Swedish massage, 100
Swift, Julia, 29
swimming, 19, 27
synovial fluid, 56

t'ai-chi, 15, 18, 167–75
taekwando, 35
tapotement, 102
teeth, 100
tendons, 36, 99, 148
tennis, 19

tension, 22, 43, 47, 49, 54, 56, 57, 59, 64, 104, 105, 116, 117, 135, 157, 158, 159, 162, 170, 188; see also stress
therapeutic touch, 98
therapist, 17, 18
throat, 14
tiredness, 135
tissue, 147, 187, 194; see also connective tissue, fascia
Tohei, Koichi, 39
touch, 101, 161, 188, 190
toxic waste, 20, 99
Trager, Milton, 193, 194
tranquillity, 46, 138, 142, 174, 176
tranquillizers, 21, 138
Transcendental Meditation, 142
transformation, 44
trauma, 54, 55, 70, 147, 155, 194
Travell, Dr Janet, 100
trigger points, 100, 107
trunk, 16, 46, 146

Ueshiba, Morihei, 33
ulcers, 100, 136
unconscious mind, 141, 194, 195
unity, 170, 176

veins, 99
verbal dialogue, 158
vibration, 102, 162
Vishnu Devananda, 176, 181
visualization, 158
vitality, 17, 20, 88, 177
Vivekananda, 176
voice, 46, 64, 71
vulnerability, 160

walking, 19
weight loss, 28
Westell, Frank, 98

white blood cells, 140
Whitehouse, Mary, 76

yang, 120
yin, 120
Yoga for Health Foundation, 180
yoga, 18, 113, 116, 122, 142,
178–85; bhakti, 177; hatha, 176,
177; karma, 176; raja, 177
Young, Philip, 121, 125, 126,
127, 128

Zen, 46
Ziehl, Silke, 159, 160